The Enchanted World

GIANTS AND OGRES

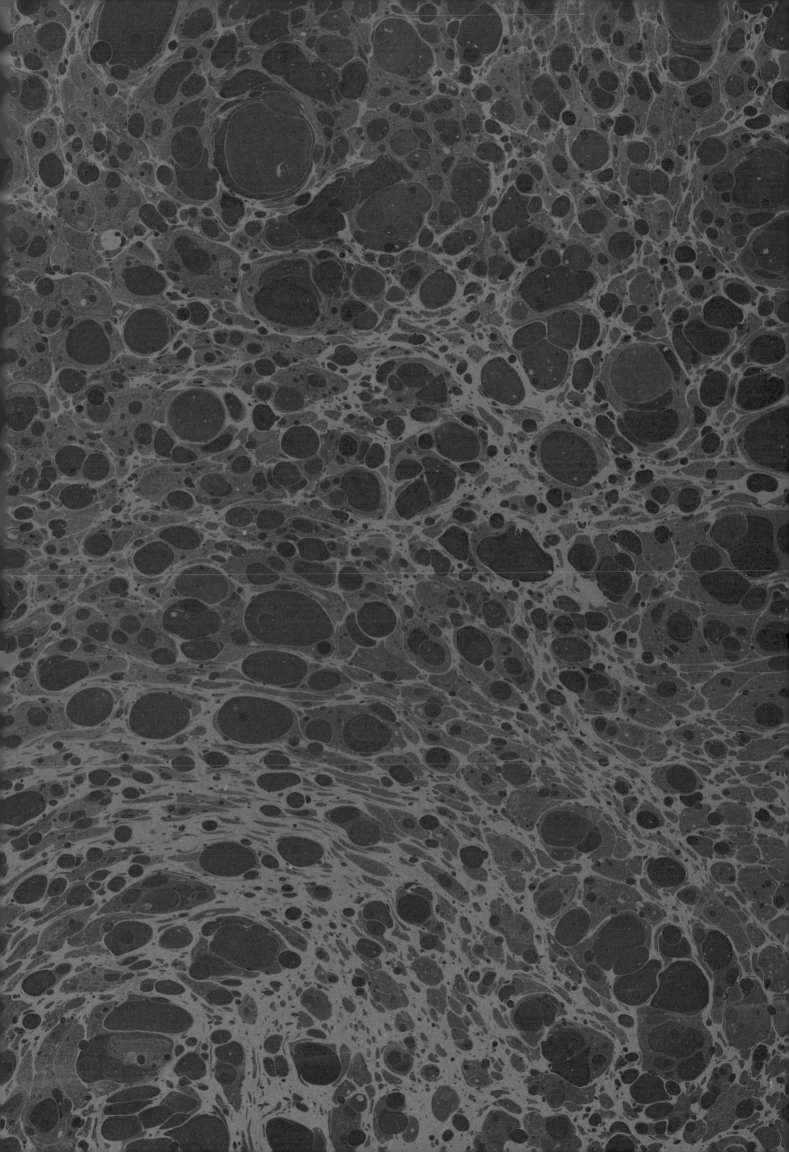

The Enchanted World

GIANTS AND OGRES

by the Editors of Time-Life Books

The Content

Time-Life Books · Amsterdam

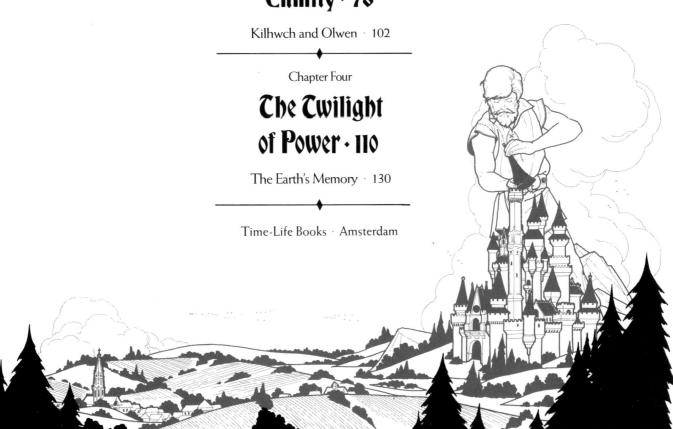

Chapter One

Princes of the Cosmos

Early one morning in March many centuries ago, when the first gentian and speedwell flowered blue in the valleys of the Tyrol, a young Austrian farmer set to work behind his plow, little dreaming that a force far greater than his ox team would soon sweep him out of his narrow world. Indeed, as the oxen trudged up and down the field and the iron wedge carved its way through the earth, he hardly thought at all. The rhythms of the work and the peacefulness of the hour wove their own reverie. Morning mist lay in the lower reaches of the valley and curled up its grassy slopes. Threads of smoke rose from the cottages of his village, a jumble of low slate roofs clinging to the valley's side and reduced to insignificance by the mountains massed around the settled lowland.

As the day wore on, the sun rose above the Alpine ridges, shining full into the valley, and the air grew warm. At the end of each furrow, the farmer halted his oxen and pushed the plow yoke forward to cool their sweating necks. Then he settled the harness and, with a slap on the oxen's flanks, turned the team into the track again and resumed his patient plodding.

Accustomed to the towering splendors of the mountains, the farmer focused on the plow, but he raised his head with a jerk when the earth trembled and a shadow fell across the length of the field. His eye could make no sense of the shape that descended swiftly toward him. Before he could dodge or even cry out, he was squeezed, front and back, by an irresistible power. He flew skyward. Beneath his kicking legs, his half-plowed field dropped sickeningly away. Village, meadow and mountain whirled briefly at the corner of his vision; clouds wheeled in white streaks above his head. Then the dizzying ascent halted, and the farmer found himself swaying seventy feet above the ground.

Gasping for breath, he stared into a pair of eyes larger than his own head and saw, reflected in their black depths, twin images of himself, a tiny figure clutched like a doll in an enormous fist. The eyes, fringed with ropy lashes, were set in a broad face filmed with red-gold hairs and beaded with saucer-sized drops of sweat. No stubble of beard showed: The creature was female.

She sighed noisily, and a blast of steamy air enveloped the farmer. After studying him for a while, she dropped him into what appeared to be a rough cloth bag. He slid down the folds of fabric, landing on a corded seam.

Moments later, an agony of buffeting and jostling began. Unable to get a purchase in his sack-prison, he rolled and tumbled in the billows of cloth. Somewhere nearby, his oxen bellowed, and from far below came the rhythmic thump of footfalls. They continued interminably. From time to time, boulders were dislodged by their impact and clattered away. The air grew icy, and the wind started to howl. Evidently he was being taken up into the mountains. All at once, the wind

ceased. An inanimate grinding sounded, as though of iron on iron, and then a great crash—a portal closing, to judge from the sudden warmth in the air. The bag was tilted, and the farmer spilled out onto what he took to be a wooden floor. He lurched to his feet and jumped away from the flailing hoofs of his oxen, which were descending toward him in the grip of a huge hand. When the beasts touched ground, the hand tightened, preventing them from bolting. Tossing their heads, the oxen showed him the whites of their eyes and bellowed dismally.

High above the farmer's head, a welter of beams and arches soared off into distant shadow. And all around him was a circle of moving monoliths. Larger than castle towers, they were human in form. Their great eyes glittered; their lips were stretched in laughter, revealing tombstone teeth and scarlet tongues. Some of them were chewing. The farmer realized that he was standing on a giant's banqueting table. Waves of unintelligible noise deafened him—speech and laughter, he surmised. He covered his ears and faced his captor. There she stood

leaning on the table, her hair falling red-gold on either side of her head.

Smiling, she stretched her enormous arm toward the farmer and carefully lifted him in one hand. With a finger, she straightened his smock and smoothed his hair. That done, she set him down. Pointing at him, she said some words in her booming voice, and peals of thunder-laughter rolled over the farmer's head.

Scarlet with rage and humiliation, the farmer shouted up at the giantess. His voice was no more than a thin squeal in the din. Yet his fury overmastered his fear, and when a finger was again poked toward him, he swung his fist at it violently.

But the hand was withdrawn, and the noise around him abated. An old man, gray-bearded and wearing a gold crown, spoke to him in a gusty whisper: "Forgive us, mortal. We mean you no harm."

Then the Giant King raised his mighty head and turned to the maiden with the red-gold hair. "Return this good man and his cattle to his own land, daughter," he said. "These are no toys for you. He is a creature of the younger race. When the last of us has gone, his kind will rule the earth that was ours."

And this was done. The farmer endured another cold and jouncing journey. As the last light of day faded, he was set down onto his own field, with his cattle and his plow. The giant maiden left him in huge, earth-shaking strides, stepping gingerly over the trees that bordered his land. He saw her one more time, years later, when a break in the Alpine mists re-vealed a large and broadly smiling face in the shadows of a mountain crevasse, watching humans live out their little lives.

If curiosity was what brought the giant-ess back to observe mortal doings, it must have been tinged with deep sadness. Giants were in decline by then. Some, it is true, were still charged with the potent magic of the first world; they served as lords and protectors of the puny humans among them. But others, like the Alpine giants, were reclusive and conservative, re-treating always from the spread of mortal civilization, clinging to their old ways in the melancholy knowledge that their race was in its twilight and a new and smaller world was approaching its noon. Many, their stock weakened, had grown brutish and feeble-minded; these ogres preyed on men and women when they could. And all were doomed to fall before the irresistible tide of human intelligence and human will, leaving nothing to mark their passage but legend and signs on the terrain — rivers whose beds they had cut, mountains they had built, vast plains they had cleared.

Yet enough men and women had seen them or talked with them or fought them or killed them to understand what the gi-ants once had been — a race that had walked among the gods.

Every country had its tales of colossi who ruled the world at the dawn of cre-ation. The Greeks, like their Hittite neigh-bors to the east, believed that Mother Earth had emerged from Chaos and cou-pled with Uranus, or Sky, to produce flowers, trees, beasts, birds and giants — the first creatures in human form. Among Earth's children were the Cyclopes, a tribe of one-eyed master smiths, and the Titans, who ruled the planets that governed the days of the week. These progeny rebelled against their father, legend said, and the youngest of them, Cronus, castrated Uranus with a sickle of adamant and thus deprived him of all his power. (The Greeks later saw Cronus as Father Time and his sickle as the instrument that cuts off the thread of every human life.)

*C*ronus then ruled the world in his father's stead. Some said his reign was a golden age and that a golden race of humans lived then; these folk flourished on a diet of wild fruit and honey, and they spent their days in dance and song. They vanished in time, as every race must, but their spirits survived as the beneficent and magical inhabitants of certain groves and trees.

Other folk, however, believed that Cronus, warned by his father that he would die at the hands of a son, ate each of his male offspring as they were born. One only escaped, through a ruse of his mother. This was Zeus, who remained hidden in the cave of Dicte on eastern Crete until he reached maturity. When he was ready, he rebelled, and in the course of his battle against Cronus, he struck his father down with a thunderbolt and confined him — with the other Titans — in hell for all eternity.

But the Titans left many descendants behind. One, Orion, could be seen in the heavens at night. He had been a mortal once — a giant son of the god Poseidon, a famous huntsman and a great lover of women. On the island of Chios, young Orion was blinded by a king whose daughter he had seduced. For healing, he walked east toward the rising sun, with a mortal man riding his shoulders as a guide. The Greeks said that the rays of the sun did indeed restore his vision; they also revealed him — the most beautiful of beings — to a nymph of the dawn and to the moon-huntress Artemis, and he became the lover of them both. Artemis, some said, killed Orion in a fit of jealousy. Then, in her grief at what she had done, she translated his corpse into stars.

She made him the loveliest constellation in the heavens, glittering with great stars of white and violet and yellow, girdled with a belt of brilliants, armed with a sword whose blade was veiled in the mist of the Great Nebula, and accompanied by shining Sirius, the Dog Star.

So splendid was Orion, in fact, that stargazers of every nation recognized him. Akkadians called him the Light of Heaven; Arabs named him al-Jabbar — the giant — or al-Bhabadur, meaning "the strong." The Hebrews said that he was Nimrod, an ancient warrior and hunter of the tribe of Ham who had been strapped to the dome of heaven for rebellion against their god. Another name sometimes given to Nimrod was Gibbor, or "giant."

The Hebrew and Arabic chroniclers told many tales of giants — descendants not of gods but of fallen angels who had taken mortal women for their wives. These giants were a vicious tribe, devourers of men. Only one of them survived the flood that covered the earth in the dim beginnings of history. This was Og.

Plucked from his field and taken to a giants' abode high in the mountains, an Austrian
farmer found himself in the role of a living toy, a plaything exhibited on a tabletop.

11

Og escaped death, wrote the scribes, because, unlike his fellows, he believed in the prophecies of the patriarch Noah about the Deluge and bound himself to serve Noah and Noah's descendants all his life. He was therefore permitted to rest beside the boxlike, three-tiered, many-chambered ark that Noah had built – from pine, according to the Hebrew chroniclers, or teak, according to the Arabic ones – when water boiled up from the earth and poured from the heavens.

The waters rose and covered all the land, and the ark floated free. It bobbed in the waves under a lowering sky, some said for forty days, and some said for a solar year – one lunar year plus eleven days. Inside the stinking chambers of the little vessel, the animals of the earth wailed and sulked; outside, in the cold and wind, Og waded. He was too large to fit into the ark, but Noah watched over him and gave him food to eat.

When at last the waters fell and the ark came to rest on Mount Ararat, the world was empty of life, save for Noah and his kin, the animals he had collected, the fish in the sea, and Og the giant. Og lived, according to the tales, for five hundred years and became King of Bashan, the mountain region east of the River Jordan, with sixty cities under his rule. In his pride, however, he ventured into Israelite territory, and there he died by mortal hands. Moses slew him in battle.

It was almost always so in mortals' tales of giants: The songs were lays of giants' demise, paeans to humankind's growing power. Few songs show the giant race in its early vigor at the morning of the world. Those that do are full of wonders, yet through each recital runs a counterpoint of elegy, as if the giants' end was present in their beginning. This was especially true in the lands of the north, where the power of the giant tribes faded more slowly than in any other place.

The people of Scandinavia described all the world in terms of their giants. The first living creature, formed from mist and frost, was the giant Ymir, who spawned a race of his own kind. Like Cronus in Greece, Ymir was slain by his own descendants, one of whom was the god Odin. Almost all the frost giants drowned in Ymir's blood.

From Ymir's great body the earth was made for mortals and set in the midst of an embracing sea. The giants who survived the slaughter of their forefather were allotted a remote territory in this world. They were driven into the northern reaches, a place of mountains and rocky wastes that was sometimes called Utgard and sometimes Jötunheim, from *jötun,* a word for giant that meant "devourer" and recalled the giants' cannibalistic habits.

In the rich center of the world rose a wall of mountains that encircled the land where humans – newly formed by Odin from ash and elm trees – dwelled. Their earth was called Midgard – literally, "boundary wall," for the wall of mountains was formed to make the earth a citadel against the ravages of the outlander giants.

High above this realm, among the clouds, floated the silver-thatched palaces of the gods. Their world, called Asgard

The giants who ruled the cosmos at the dawn of time feared the beings born after them;
thus the Titan Cronus devoured his sons so that they might not become his conquerors.

Guided by a mortal, the giant Orion searched for the healing light of dawn.

after Aesir, the collective name for the race of gods, was linked to earth by the rainbow bridge, Bifrost.

The old songs are full of accounts of how the gods crossed this bridge to guard the humans they had made; the thunder-god Thor, in fact, was named for his position as Midgard's warder (*veorr*, in the old tongue) against the giants. Even the gods in the first flush of their might, however, used caution in their dealings with the ancestors

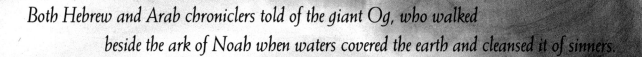

Both Hebrew and Arab chroniclers told of the giant Og, who walked beside the ark of Noah when waters covered the earth and cleansed it of sinners.

of all living things. The giants then were haughty and warlike; in their cold veins flowed the blood of magic; they were masters of changing shape and of illusion; and they were charged with the wisdom of the most ancient things. Encounters with the giants were fraught with danger, as an early story shows.

The tale concerns Thor and a journey he made to match himself against the elder race. Called the Thunderer, the Giant Killer, the Friend to Man, Thor was one of the great gods. He traveled often through the earth that he protected. At the time of this tale, he had for a companion

Loki – a perilous companion, indeed. Loki dwelled among the gods and was counted as a lesser god himself; he had the beauty of an elf, but the shifting, dangerous nature of fire. Sly and tricksy, he often called himself Lopt, meaning "airy one," and he was never to be trusted. With this pair traveled two servants, a human boy named Thialfi and a girl named Roskva.

The little company traveled through the rich north of Midgard, skirting its flat green fields and forest-lined lakes and making for the rocky, snow-strewn crags

Norse gods were the first challengers of giants, although the size of the old ones gave them pause. On one adventure, Thor and three companions made camp in a giant's glove.

that formed its barrier against the wilder shores of the earth. By nightfall of the second day, they were ascending into the mountain passes. When the shadows grew long, the four looked about them for a place to make camp.

In the midst of a stand of alder, near the long and jagged ridge of the mountain, they found a well-made hide shelter, the summer retreat, perhaps, of a shepherd— or of several shepherds, for the hut had a central cavelike chamber and five branching rooms. A rank smell drifted from its wide, dark mouth. The human children hesitated at the entrance, and Loki gave them orders with irritation. He had a quick, sharp temper and little use for humans. Eventually, the children built a small hearth fire near the entrance; it helped to drive the smell away. The company ate then and slept, well shielded from the night winds of the mountains.

They were awakened by the trembling of the ground beneath them. Their shelter rocked crazily to and fro. Thor leaped through the door, and the others stumbled after him. An amazing sight greeted them there. The nearby mountain ridge buckled upward. It was, in

fact, no ridge but an immense being who now rose heavily to his feet, towering against the morning sky.

Golden Thor, girt with a belt that gave him power and armed with his thunder hammer, spoke fearlessly: "The Thunderer, warden of Midgard, gives greeting."

At Thor's words, the giant sank to his haunches so that his face came into view. For some moments, he gazed at the god from heavy-lidded eyes. Then he said softly, "Are the conquerors so tiny?" "We have strength you know not of, old one," Thor answered. "Then follow me, if you would test it," said the gi-

ant. "I am Skrymir." He reached behind the little company where they stood and flicked their shelter into his hands: The place they had spent the night was his leather glove, and their supplies were still in it. Straightening again, he set off northward, down the mountain where he had slept. Soon he was far away, loping easily across the broad, bracken-covered plain that lay at the base of Midgard's wall, heading toward the forests of his home.

"We follow Skrymir," said Thor. The children muttered anxiously, but Loki merely shrugged and said, "No wonder the shelter stank so." Then the four set off to follow the giant's track. They had a hard march. In that land the winds moaned

ceaselessly, and the sky spat icy rain. The ground was littered with rocks, and the scrub that covered it bristled with thorns. The pursuers had, of course, no food. The children grew silent and sullen, and Loki grew more acid-tongued; only Thor kept an even temper. He marched tirelessly, and the others straggled behind.

They found Skrymir at nightfall, stretched out along the ground at the edge of Utgard's forest. He raised a derisive eyebrow when he saw them, but he made no comment on the slowness of such small beings. He said only that he had fed and that their food was in his provisions sack. Then he closed his eyes and paid them no further notice. After a while, he began to snore, rattling the branches of the trees.

The children backed away. Loki snarled wordlessly. Thor, however, paced the length of the mighty body to the feet, where the giant's provisions sack lay beside a boulder. He inspected it. The stiff leather bundle was the size of a peasant's hut, and it was bound with a heavy thong. With a sigh, the thunder-god climbed the boulder and grasped the end of the thong to free the knot.

Swift as a serpent, the thong contracted, coiling more tightly around the neck of the sack. The loose end whistled from Thor's hand. He tried again, and again the thong jerked away and jealously squeezed at the sack.

This was giants' magic. Thor could not defeat it. He strode to Skrymir's head and shouted the giant's name.

The ancient creature stirred no more than a stone. Loki sniggered at Thor's powerlessness, and the thunder-god paled with rage. Then he drew his hammer from his belt. He raised it, and lightning glittered at its head as it felt the fury of the god within it. The hammer flew down to the dome of the giant's head, ringing as it descended to shatter the skull.

But at the impact, Skrymir only shifted a little in his sleep and muttered. The hammer had not even broken his skin. The girl Roskva, half-blinded by the lightning flash, began to weep, and

Loki, for once, was silent. What creature was this that lived and yet could withstand the weaponed anger of the heavens?

Twice more that night Thor struck the giant with the hammer that had made whole villages explode in flame.

Each stroke glanced off the heavy-boned skull, eliciting no more than drowsy mumbles from the giant. When dawn came and he awoke, however, he smiled narrowly upon his small companions, and told them he had dreamed of leaves and acorns falling on his head. Thor said only, "Guide us now to the halls of Jötunheim, old one." He had no wish to face others of Skrymir's ilk, whose strength was proof against the gods even in sleep, but he had no choice: Thor was the warden of Midgard, and all its people were in his care. "With-

in the wood you will find a river," Skrymir replied. "Follow its course and take the track that runs east from the second turning. That leads to my brothers' hall, and you may enter, if you dare. My path takes me another way; you and I will meet no more." And without another word, Skrymir rose and strode north across the plain toward the now-distant mountains.

The journey of Thor and his companions was swift. By noon, the four stood un-

Even Thor's hammer of heaven, a weapon that could destroy whole villages with thunderbolts, had no effect on Skrymir. But this, too, was giants' magic, needed against the growing power of gods and men.

der the vault of Jötunheim's great fortress and greeted the giant they found there. He was the lord of that place. He was old, as old as frost and mist and ice. His hair and beard were silver, his wrinkled skin was gray, and all color was bleached from his shadowed eyes. He spoke wearily, in the cracked voice of the aged, but his tone was conciliatory. He gave the adventurers the freedom of his palace, presented them to the enormous warriors of his court, and feasted them on a royal scale.

The feast was typical of the age, abundant, drunken and noisy, but it stirred fear in the travelers from Asgard. When the drink had gone round many times, the hosts challenged the visitors to contests to test their strength — not trials by com-

bat, but the contests men in their cups were in the habit of holding then. The first contest was to see who could drink the most in one draught. Thor, with a god's capacity, represented the visitors, but he lost. Next, they competed for the honor of eating most, and swaggering Loki lost to a voracious member of the Giant King's company. They held a foot race, and the human boy Thialfi failed in his attempt. The hall rang with the laughter of the giants in the end, and even swift-tongued Loki quailed before the giants' strength and kept his silence.

In the morning, the Giant King escorted his visitors through the gates of the fortress, moving hardly at all so as not to precede those with shorter strides. As he stepped onto the track, Thor turned to bid farewell, and said, "Good King, we did not know your power. I have failed, and feel the danger to those whom I must guard."

But the Giant King smiled a cold and secret smile, and said, "Had we known your own strength, Thunderer, you would never have passed these walls. And never will you pass through again, for you hold our deaths in your hands. Your defeats were made by trickery, so that while you were among us you would not realize your might and do us injury." The old giant swayed and trembled above the god; his features wavered and for a moment showed the red beard and heavy-lidded eyes of Skrymir. Then the Giant King — who had indeed been their guide to

The first giants were masters at changing shape—and none more so than Thiassi, who became an eagle and dragged the god Loki across mountain crag and glacier until he divulged the secret of immortality.

this place—told how he had tempted Thor to the hammer blows and, by magic, interposed a rocklike shield of mountains' strength between the hammer and his head. He told how Thor's drinking horn drew water from the sea and how the tides receded when the god took his draught; he told how Loki's opponent in eating was all-consuming fire in giant's guise; how Thialfi's running foe was the Giant King's own swift thought made incarnate.

In reply, the Thunderer drew forth his hammer. It flashed in his hand, but even as he raised it, the giant faded to transparency and disappeared. The walls of the fortress shimmered and, as if melting, slid toward the earth and spread and trembled. The god stood no more before the stronghold of his enemy: A green and flowering valley spread out where the fortress of the giants had been. Seeing the vigor of the younger beings, the rulers of the oldest race had made a wall of invisibility to keep themselves safe from Thor and all his kind.

So in their northern exile the ancients lived on, and rumors about the region and its awesome inhabitants trickled past the boundaries of Midgard and entered the chronicles of humankind. A river called Ifing encircled the heart of the giants' land, it was said, and this river never froze. Within its confines, many tribes of giants appeared—descendants, perhaps, of the original frost giants.

Little more than their names and vague descriptions reached the ears of men and women, but these were frightening enough. The 12th Century Danish historian Saxo, called Grammaticus, or "learned," wrote that the giants were shaggy monsters, able to shift size and shape. Some had many arms, some many heads. The harsh mountains of Utgard also sheltered giants connected with rocks; among their number were creatures who had heads and hearts of stone, and who bore stone shields and fought with stone swords. And scattered amid the northern mountains were volcanoes that served as the burial places of fire-giants. It was widely believed that, at the end of time, these would be in the vanguard when long-buried giants rose against the gods and that the fire they made would eventually consume the world. Any volcanic eruption was said to be caused by giants.

A venerable forest grew in Utgard, too. It was named Iarnvith, or "Ironwood," and in the shadows of its trees, often shrouded in enchanted mists, wild giants with names such as Vitholf (Wolf of the Wood) and Welderich (Lord of the Wood) dwelled. Because of the presence of these woodmen and woodwomen, who were powerful and jealous of the trees under their protection, no timber was cut in that forest.

Even the cold waters off the Utgard shore were perilous. Corpse-hungry giants lay in wait there for ships that sank in winter storms. Tales of all these creatures—sometimes garbled, often contradictory and always frightening—were enough to keep the men and women of Midgard from crossing their mountain boundary into the

Neary

His mighty wings devoured by flames, his eagle's body split by lance and ax,
Thiassi perished at the hands of the gods in Asgard, their stronghold in the
clouds. In time, even mortals would aspire to the conquest of such formidable foes.

wildernesses of Utgard. And it was rare that giants ventured into the world of men: Although strong in body and in magic, they were clothed in mortality. The end of their race was approaching, and the executioners were the shining ones, the ever-young gods of Asgard, who protected humankind. So great was the prowess of the gods in their golden age that – in contrast to the tale of Thor and Skrymir – they were almost always able to best the giants.

Such a story was that of Thiassi, an ice giant who was a master at changing shape. Unlike his fellows, Thiassi journeyed frequently across the mountain wall of Midgard, riding the frigid winds in the form of an enormous eagle. Sharp-eyed and fearsomely taloned, he was a formidable predator. Once he even defied the power of the gods, although he soon rued his boldness.

The god Thiassi chose to challenge was Loki, the trickster, who happened to be idling about in the world of men. Thiassi spied him from on high; he saw the ox the god was roasting, and he snatched it for himself. But Thiassi had not reckoned on Loki's quickness. Like lightning, the god struck back. He buried the blade of his battle staff in Thiassi's feathered bosom.

The eagle-giant howled with pain, and in his howling, he cried runes of binding, so that the blade stayed fast in his own flesh – and Loki's hands stayed fast to the shaft of the spear. Then, with the god his prisoner, Thiassi leaped into the air.

High above the trees of Midgard he flew, rolling and tumbling on the wind and wrenching the god's arms in their sockets. He dropped lower to drag Loki through tree branches, into glacial mountain lakes and across hillsides bristling with gorse. Only when Loki screamed that he would surrender anything for his freedom did Thiassi desist.

"Bring me the apples of Idun," he said, and released Loki at the base of the rainbow bridge that led to the gods' land.

It was a cunning command. Idun was a goddess as lovely as life itself, and in her care were golden apples that gave the gods eternal youth. Fed on them, a giant might achieve immortality, and the goddess herself was a prize worth having.

Loki, who had no loyalty and a fine regard for his own well-being, did as he was told, seeking out Idun in her silver-thatched hall, where the breezes of Asgard sang among the columns for her. He told her that golden apples to match her own had been found in a grove in Midgard.

Idun suspected nothing. She took her treasure and followed Loki over Bifrost and into the world of humankind, where the eagle Thiassi waited. He caught her up in his talons and flew into the clouds, heading for his mountain aerie. Loki returned to Asgard, saying nothing, naturally enough, about what he had done.

But the theft was noticed almost at once. Bereft of the life-giver, the company of heaven began to fade and wither. And the servant of Heimdall the White, watchman to the gods and ever the trickster's enemy, had seen Loki at his work. When the servant told what he had witnessed, the gods turned on Loki and ordered him to find Idun and bring her safely home.

Loki refused. He had already suffered the strength of Thiassi. So the gods threatened him with an apt punishment — spread-eagling. This was a form of torture commonly used in sacrifices in Midgard: The victim was bound with his face to a tree; then, one by one, his ribs were cut free from the flesh of his back and pulled up on either side of his spine to form "wings." Faced with this ghastly fate, the trickster had no choice but to accept the gods' command. He was given a magic falcon skin that endowed him with the gift of flight.

Far above Bifrost, Loki flew, across the fields of Midgard and into the mountains. All day he wheeled and banked, searching with sharp falcon's eyes for the lair of Thiassi. At dusk, he spied a cave mouth among the peaks on the giants' side of Midgard's border. A ribbon of hearth smoke issued from the entrance.

The falcon banked and swooped into the cave. Golden Idun was within, but there was no sign of Thiassi. In a high falcon's mew, Loki recited runes of changing, and the goddess, with her apples in her hands, dwindled to the size of a hazelnut. Loki picked her up in his beak and launched himself southward.

Like an arrow through the darkening sky the falcon sped, passing high over the fields of Midgard. Behind him, a scream rent the air: Thiassi had seen him and taken to the air to give chase.

Loki made for the fading glow of Bifrost where it arched toward the rosy sky far in the distance. Behind him, the eagle screamed again, rowing the air powerfully with its great wings. A much larger bird than the falcon, it gained quickly on its prey and began to climb above Loki, getting height for the kill.

The falcon reached the luminous bridge and soared along its arch up into the gates of Asgard. The gods were waiting there, visibly older and weaker than when Loki had left them. Loki shed his falcon form and gave Idun her shape again. He gasped a warning, but the shining ones had seen the eagle high above, and they were ready to do battle. Thiassi hurtled down from the heavens, breaching the very gates of Asgard, his talons extended.

He never struck. The defenders thrust torches up into his wings, and the golden feathers crackled into flame. Thiassi plummeted to the floor of Asgard. The gods swarmed over him, hacking and stabbing amid the flames until nothing was left of the eagle-giant but a shapeless mass of smoking flesh and splintered bones.

Thus died the enemy of the gods, who dared to challenge them on their own ground. It was but one death of many as the giant race began its decline. The time would come when the giant kingdoms would be sundered, not by gods but by human beings, leaving only patches of enchanted territory to shelter solitary giants whose days of glory were long past.

Even as their power diminished, however, the giants preserved among themselves the shadowy bequest of the first age of the earth. Although their numbers and their stature shrank, there remained in them something of the fierce lordliness of old, when giants were the fathers of all that lived on earth.

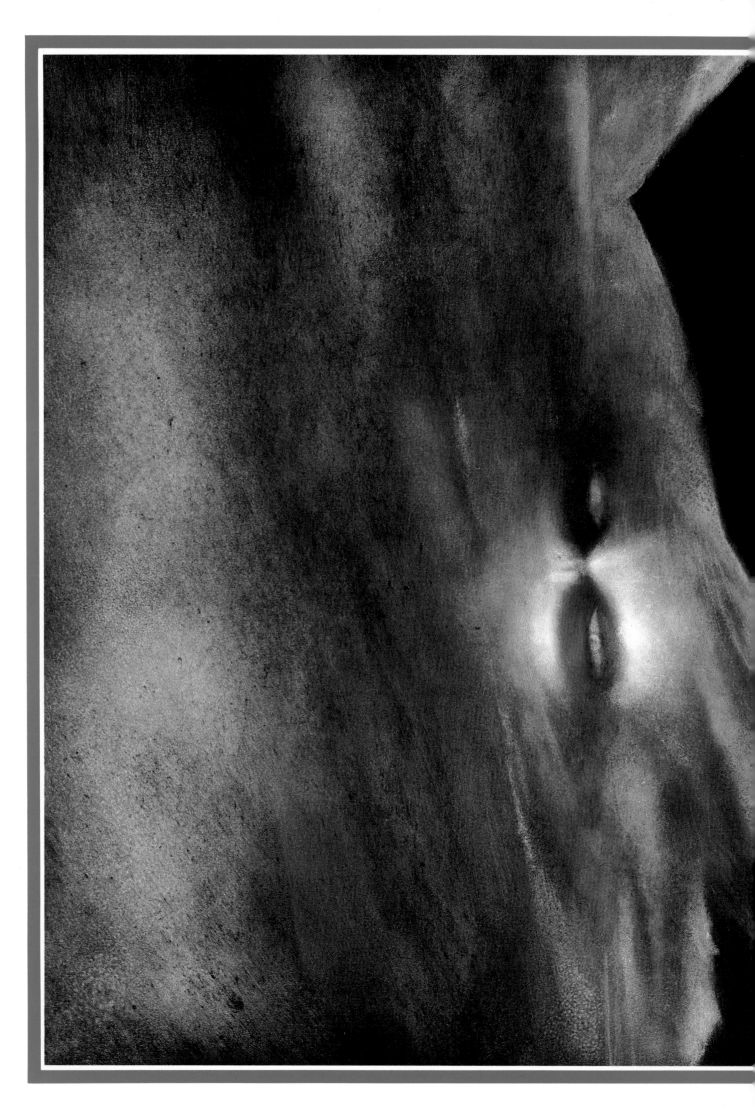

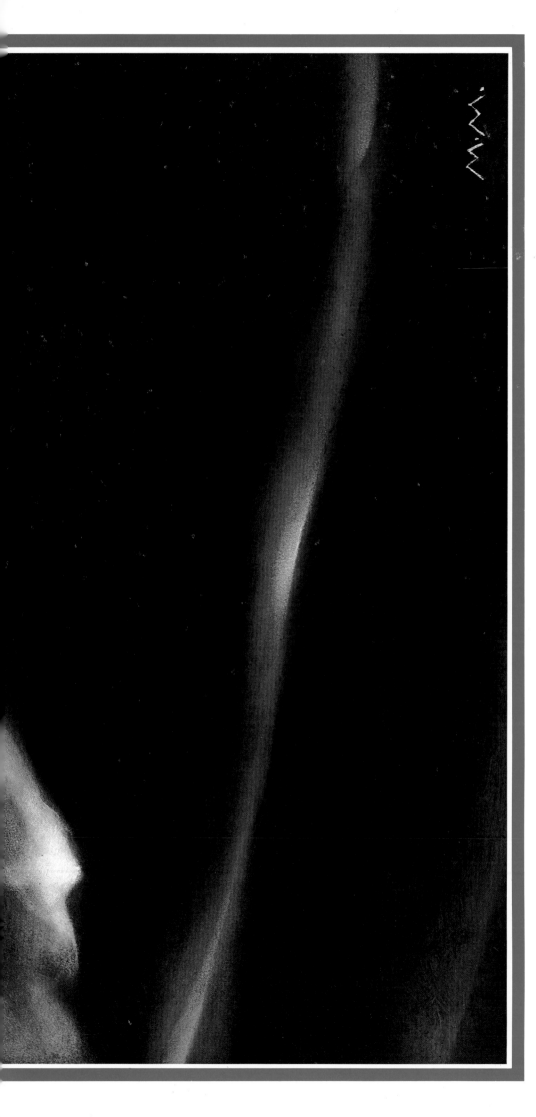

The Heirs of the First World

The earliest giants were true sons of heaven, arising from a mist-shrouded chaos
at the beginning of time. In ancient Norse belief, the first creature to
stir in the cosmos was the frost giant Ymir, born of the warring kingdoms of fire
and ice when stray sparks melted a glacial floe and quickened it
into life. Ymir's body spawned a whole race of frost giants, and their offspring,
the gods, soon followed. In time, the hoary progenitor of all living
beings was sacrificed, to create the ordered universe of earth and sea and sky.
Many and varied were the giant descendants of Ymir, as these pages
show, but all came to eventual grief – undone by the gods or fate or humankind.

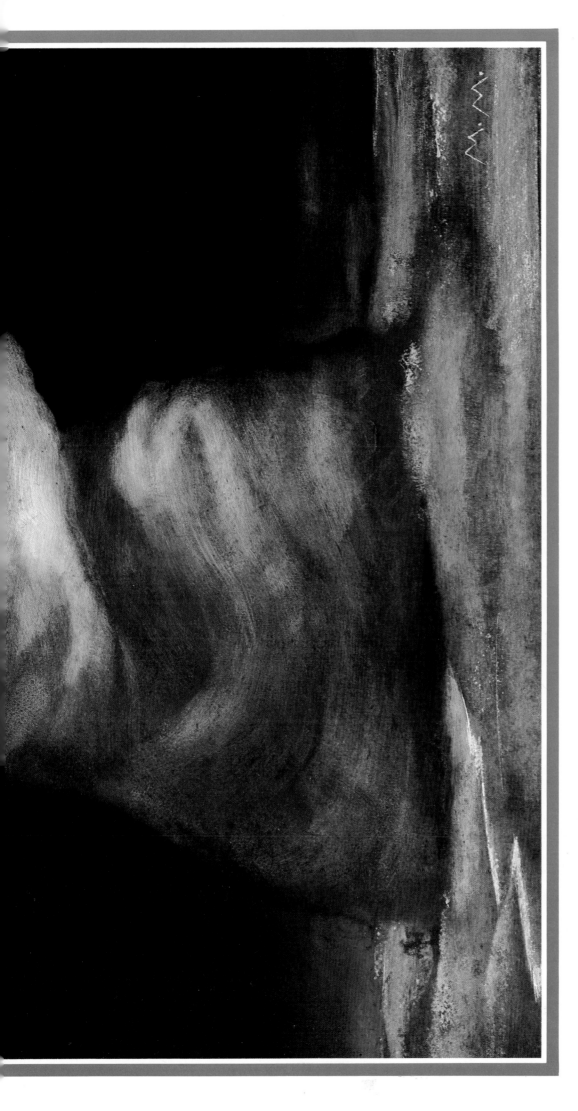

Pillar of the heavens

In punishment for mutiny against
the gods of Greece, the Titan Atlas was con-
demned to spend all eternity as a
living pillar. With massive arms he held back
the starry curtain of the heavens,
so that it would not fall and crush the fragile
earth. His name fitted his task:
Atlas meant "enduring."

A torpid terror

A formidable sleeper was the giant Kumbhakarna, fearsome warrior of Hindu
legend. A mountain was his pillow, and heaven
rattled with his snores. When the armies
of evil needed him in battle, they found that
waking Kumbhakarna was a battle all its
own. It took the sting of lances, blaring horns
and torrents of cold water to rouse him.

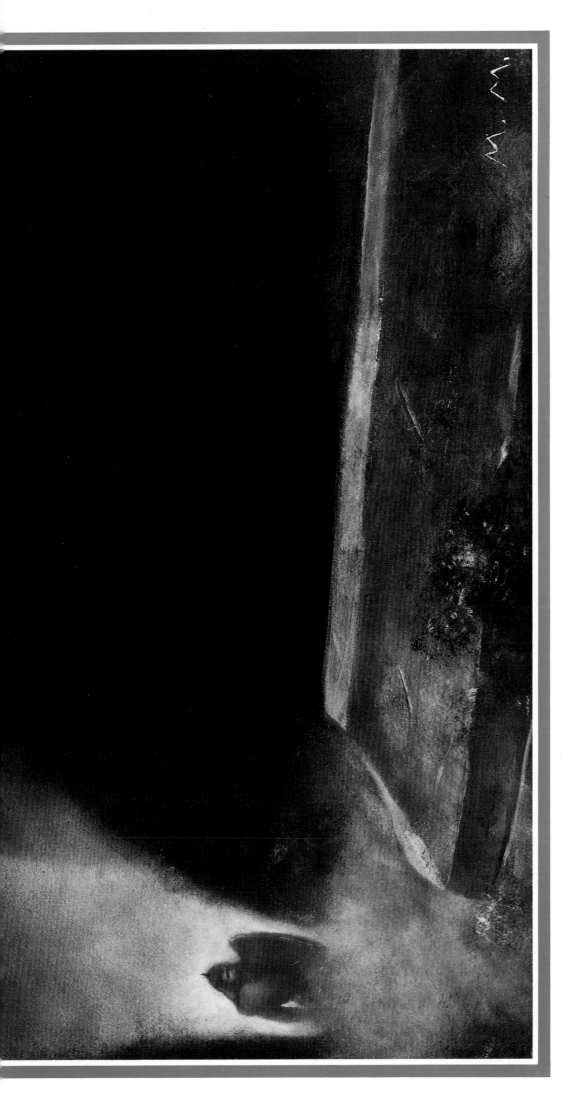

A Russian behemoth

His weight too great for marshy lowlands to bear, a mischievous giant named Svyatogor roamed the granitic mountain heights of Russia. His end was piteous: Accompanied by a human friend, he came upon a mighty coffin and, laughing, shut himself inside. But the jest was his undoing, for no mortal could lift the lid.

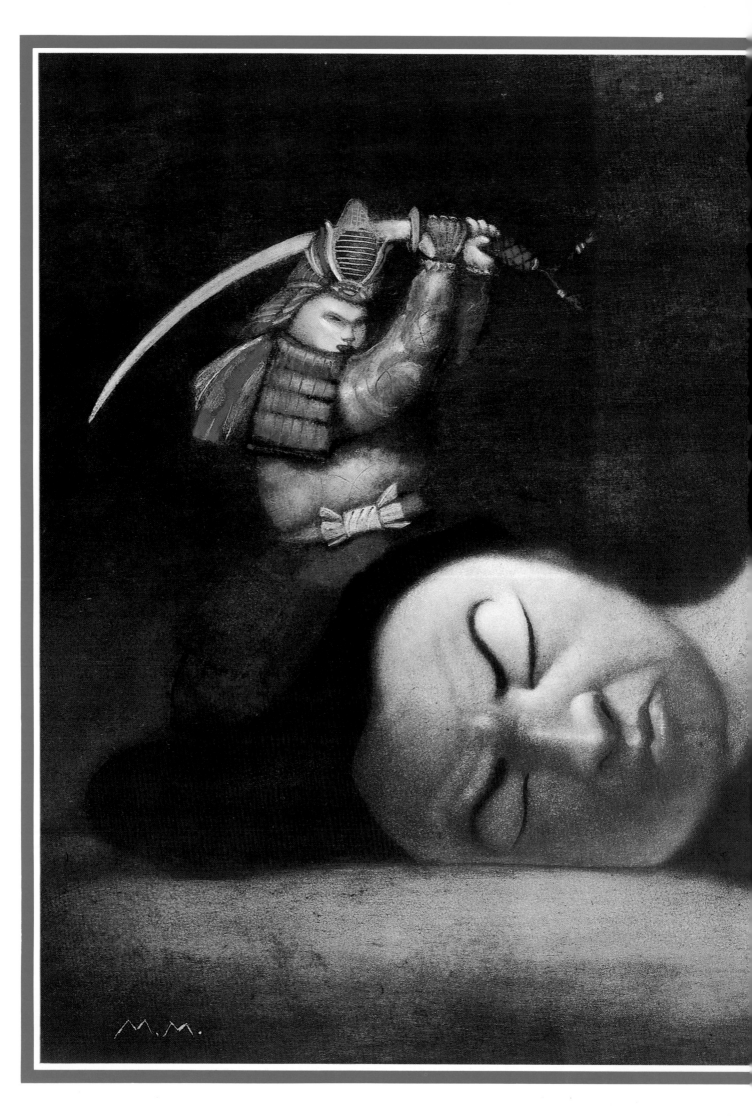

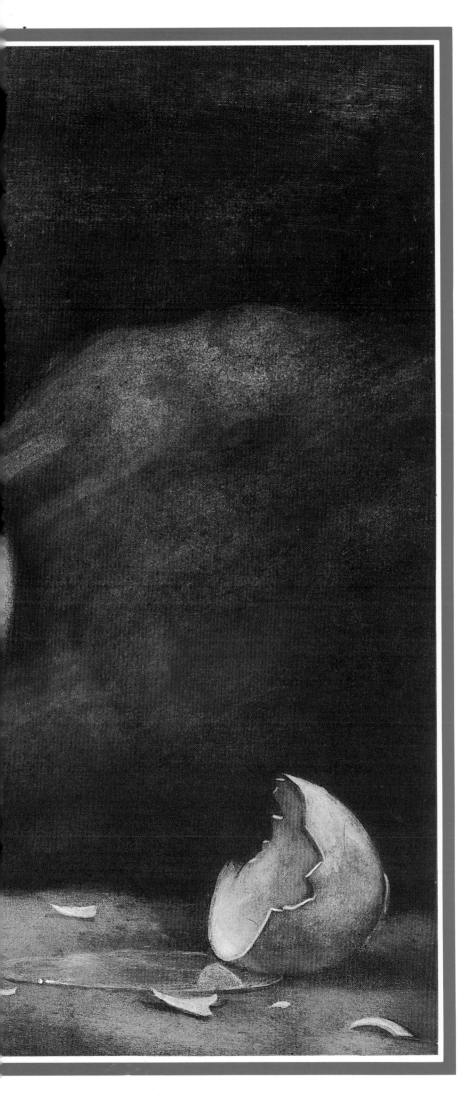

Deathmonger of the East

In old Japan, no outlaw was more
feared than the ogre Shutendoji, who kid-
napped innocent striplings and
feasted on their flesh. Finally, a wily warlord
named Raiko tracked the giant to his
lair near Kyoto and slyly drugged his wine.
And then the hero beheaded him.

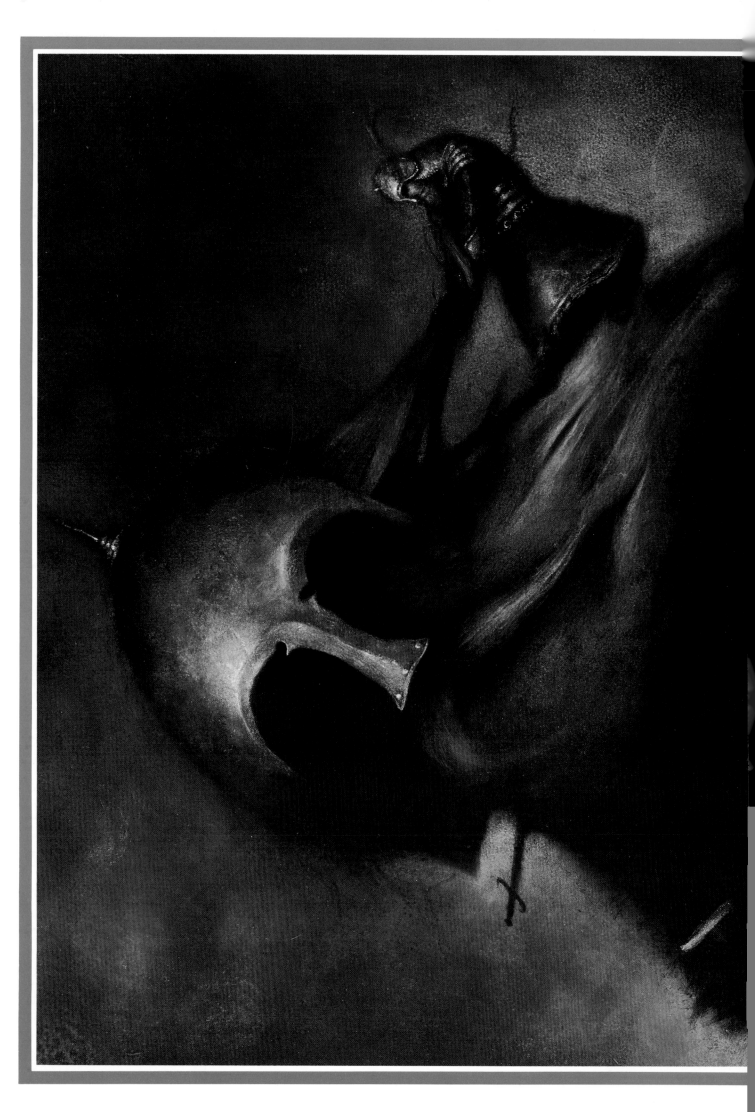

A watching head

In elder ages, some giants acted as guardians of treasure. Thus, an enchanted giant's head, severed from its trunk but living still, long lay upon a Russian battlefield, guarding a magic sword. The hero Ruslan dealt the death blow to the head, then toppled it to take the sword, which served as his weapon against the forces of evil.

Chapter Two

Protectors and Providers

To the fishermen of Somerset and Devon, souvenirs of the earliest age of the earth were once as familiar as friends. Behind their coastal villages towered the headlands of Exmoor, a wind-swept and curlew-haunted wilderness that, in the distant past, had been part of a Celtic kingdom called Dummonia. On its heather-covered moors and wooded slopes were the remains of the ancient chieftains' hill forts, no more now than grassy mounds ringed with earthworks. The Celtic roundhouses were reduced to clusters of crumbling stones, and the Celts themselves lay hidden in turf-covered funeral barrows, their bones adorned with golden collars and armlets of bronze. But a relic of that age—a

giant—still walked on Exmoor many centuries after Dummonia disappeared. While reclusive, in the manner of the wild beasts among which he sheltered, he was occasionally observed by the fishermen who sailed the waters of the Bristol Channel far below his forest and heath.

The giant had no name that the humans knew, but certain facts about him were well established. He was said to live in the northeastern corner of Exmoor, at the meeting of the Brendon and Quantock Hills. His own particular dwelling place was called Grabbist Hill—an appropriate site, since the giant was a gentle creature and the hill is peaceful and pretty, wooded with oak, beech and holly on the steep lower slopes and crowned with purple heather. At the base of Grabbist is a village called Dunster, with a handsome castle and a river running beside it. From the summit of the hill, the waters of the channel can be seen, shimmering in the distance.

The villagers of Dunster spoke fondly of the giant of Grabbist. Aged and remote, he made no attempt to know them, but he watched over the village and moors from his aerie. If the children waved to him, he waved back and, it was said, this created a breeze that dried the washing hung out on lines.

The giant's presence was protection. No thieves threatened the villagers' sheep and cattle; no outlaws crept into their streets at night. And when the need arose, he served as more than a watchman, as various Somerset tales relate.

It was said, for instance, that the giant fed on fish. His method of catching them was simple: He would walk carefully across the moors and hills to the harbor at the village of Minehead and wade far out into the waters of the channel, scanning for pilchard and herring. When he reached the shoals, he scooped up the fish in his great hands and ate them where he stood. The ones he did not eat—and these were many—he poured into any little fishing boat that bobbed nearby.

The Grabbist giant guarded the fisherfolk just as he did the inland villagers. A man named Elijah Crowcombe could testify to this. Crowcombe left his home harbor one morning with a crew of two, heading out to sea under a blue sky and racking clouds. His vessel, like those of his neighbors, was rowed, not sailed: Oars gave the control needed in those choppy waters. Unlike his neighbors' dinghies, however, Crowcombe's boat, *Dorcas Jane*, was old and leaky; he was a careless seaman.

He almost lost his life and those of his companions that day. His boat was well out from land when a mass of gray gathered on the horizon, signaling a squall's approach. Crowcombe and his men turned and pulled hard for the harbor as soon as they saw the storm, but there was little chance of reaching safety. The sky darkened rapidly. The squall hit like an invisible hammer, blinding the men with spray and rain, tossing the dinghy on tenfoot seas. Soon the little craft was half full of water. An oar snapped in the wild waves and was lost.

Then from the boiling mist, a huge hand emerged. It closed around the boat and lifted her above the savage seas. Another hand appeared and spread out over the men to shelter them from the blast of the storm. In this warm cocoon, they rode back to their village. The dinghy was lowered into the sheltered waters of the harbor. Then the giant of Grabbist knelt on the headland and watched gravely while the men dragged the boat to shore. In a moment, satisfied that not even a fishing basket had been lost, he rose and strode up to Exmoor and his hill.

How long the giant kept watch over Exmoor and the seamen of Somerset remains uncertain. He simply faded from human sight. But this benign creature of sea and hill and forest left a token of his tenure—a bridge that he was said to have built by hand. An affair of immense stone slabs resting on rock piers, it crosses the River Barle in the center of Exmoor, stretching 180 feet to connect a trackway once used by the Celts.

The Grabbist giant was a late manifestation of an old truth. Giants were not in themselves evil, nor were they always the enemies of the races that succeeded them. In the beginning, they were as much a part of creation as gods and men. Indeed, they were the ancestors of both, and bearers of the oldest wisdoms.

In the days when the northern gods flourished in Asgard, this was understood. Giant tribes were, of course, isolated in their own land of Utgard at the borders of the new-made world, and there was enmity between them and the gods. But the old ones were recognized and honored as part of the rightful order of things.

Never was this shown more clearly than during the time of the gods' worst tragedy, when the grief of all things living shook the foundations of the earth. That tragedy was the death of Balder. The story, in brief, was this:

Son of the All-father, Odin, Balder was beloved among the gods. He was the best of them, graceful of speech, fine of judgment and so handsome that light shone from his body. In the prime of his years, he was assailed by evil dreams of his own death, and the gods, therefore, took an oath from each thing of earth and sea and sky—every animal, every plant, every wind—that it would not harm this fairest of their sons. All swore except the mistletoe: The plant was not asked to swear because it was new to the earth and thought too young to be a cause for worry.

Then the richly gifted god was safe; his fellows even made a game of attacking him, and they all found him invincible—all of them, that is, but Loki, the trickster, the lurking god, who hated what was beautiful and loved what gave pain. Discovering that the mistletoe was Balder's bane, he made from its boughs a spear. He tricked Balder's brother, the blind god Hoder, into casting the spear at Balder, and he even gave Hoder direction for throwing. In this way, Balder was slain.

The world wept—except, of course, Loki, who fled. The gods bore Balder's body to the edge of the world-embracing sea and laid it on the shore where *Ringhorn*, his great curving battleship, rested on a row of logs that would be used to roll it into the waters.

The whole company of heaven and earth was there to mourn. Close by Odin were ranged the Valkyries, his battle goddesses. Frey, god of sun and rain and growing things, was there, standing tall in his chariot and holding the reins of a golden-bristled boar. Beside him in a chariot drawn by cats was his sister Freya, goddess of love. Around these and the other gods surged a crowd of gray dwarfs and shimmering elves. And looming behind them, pale with sorrow, came the frost giants, starry with their clouds of ice and snow, and the stone giants of Utgard.

A giantess named Hyrrokin pushed the ship *Ringhorn* over its rollers into the sea.

She stood in the shallows while Balder's body was placed on its bier amidships. The fallen god was joined by the body of his wife, who had died of grief. When all was ready, Odin, the great lord, whispered secret words in his dead son's ear. Finally, the ship, heavy with funeral treasure, was set alight and sent toward the deeps to disappear in a ring of fire.

All the company dispersed — the gods to their cloud country, dwarfs and elves to earth, and the giants to Utgard. Thereafter, the old enmities between the gods and giants were resumed, for the giants possessed something that the gods greatly desired: As the elders of creation, they held the wisdom of earth, sea and sky. Their all-knowingness was part of their terribleness and their power.

Some of this wisdom originated beneath Yggdrasil, the colossal, invisible world tree whose branches stretched into the heavens and whose roots penetrated through the earth into the depths of hell. One of its roots, which twisted under the soil of the giants' land, sheltered a spring whose waters gave the drinker insight into the nature of all things. The spring was guarded by the head of the giant Mimir, which had been severed by the gods in an early battle but restored to life by Odin, because he wished to learn its secrets. Odin traded one of his eyes to Mimir for a single drink from the waters of the spring. In this way, he drained a portion of the wisdom of the ages.

But he was not yet satisfied. Some knowledge was hidden in runes — literally "mysteries," or charms — known only to the giants. These Odin gathered to himself by many means. His own most famous account of his search for wisdom told how he hanged himself and pierced his own side with a spear — a sacrifice of himself to himself, a journey through death in search of its secrets. "For nine nights," he recited, "I hung on the wind-swept tree." At last, he died howling. But when the ordeal was ended, he rose again from the dead as Father of Magic and Lord of the Gallows, having heard nine songs of giants and learned the runic charms that could conquer pain, cure sickness, blunt his enemies' blades, free himself from any fetters, stop arrows' flight, turn aside evil spells, uproot hatred from men's minds, calm storms at sea, capture practitioners of evil magic, sing battle companions into bravery, make hanged men tell the secrets of their deaths, bless children so that when they grew they would be invincible in war, tell the hidden names of all the gods and elves, and capture the hearts of women and keep them faithful.

most people thought that the tree on which Odin hanged himself was the world tree, Yggdrasil, which acquired its name from Odin's ordeal. Yggdrasil meant "the horse of the terrible one": Gallows trees were called "horses" in the north, and "the terrible one" was a name for Odin.

The god had other means of wresting wisdom from living giants. On one occasion, he journeyed to Utgard in disguise to trick from the giant Vafthrudnir the understanding of the beginning and the end of the world. Not recognizing the god,

A mighty benefactor

Perhaps because they were outcasts themselves, giants sometimes showed great compassion toward mortals tossed roughly aside by fate or by their fellows. Here is one such tale:

A rich Russian merchant had three sons. The first two he endowed with sleek trading vessels, but for the youngest, Ivan by name, there was only a creaky ship with a ragged sail. Yet Ivan's trading prospered, until his ship's hold groaned with gold and a fair lady joined him on his journeying. His success did him no good with his brothers, however. The eldest coveted his maiden, the other his treasure. Together they attacked his ship and threw Ivan overboard.

Ivan drifted with the current until he washed up on a bleak and unfamiliar shore. A shaggy giant, whose gnarled staff stood taller than a ship's mast, stood waiting on the shingle.

Even in his exhaustion Ivan could still feel fear. "Lord," he cried out, "Spare me!"

The tale does not say what cruel twist of fortune had brought the giant to this desolate strand, but it must have been such that it bound him in sympathy to the tiny castaway. For he did more than spare the intruder: He swung him up onto his lofty shoulder and waded into the sea, bearing Ivan safely to his own country.

Ivan was quick to reclaim his lady and his treasure. And though the giant soon returned to his lonely haunt, the man he had stooped to save never forgot him: Ivan told his story so many times that the legend of the giant's mercy became known to all of Russia.

Vafthrudnir entered into a contest of wits with him. The stakes were high: Each contestant wagered his life. But Vafthrudnir was arrogant in his vast knowledge. He knew all the runes of the gods and of men and had himself visited the land of the dead. Thinking to defeat his opponent at once, he challenged the god to tell him the secret names of great things—of the stallion that drew the light of day across the sky, for instance. That name was Skinfaxi, and Odin knew it. Vafthrudnir asked more names, and Odin knew them, too. Then it was the god's turn to question.

From Vafthrudnir, Odin learned how earth, sky and sea had been created from the flesh, skull and blood of the giant Ymir. He learned the names of the fathers of the moon and sun, of winter and summer. He learned that the winds came from the eagle Hraesvelg, called the Corpse-eater because it devoured the dead. The eagle sat alone at the edge of heaven, fanning the air with its wings.

Odin also learned of Ragnarök—or "the doom of the gods." Discord among the gods—the kind of discord that led to the death of Balder—would rouse the snows and winds. In the midst of a winter three years long, the earth would sink into the sea. All the gods and almost all humanity would die, and then fire from the sunken earth would destroy the world. Only two mortal creatures would survive that terrible time: a man named Lif and a woman named Lifthraser, who would hide in the great ash Yggdrasil and live to repopulate the world.

All these profound wonders Odin learned from the giant Vafthrudnir, and when the god was satisfied, he asked a question the giant could not answer. What, Odin asked, had the All-father whispered into the ear of his son Balder when Balder lay on his funeral pyre? Then Vafthrudnir recognized that he had lost his wager, for no one but the god himself could know the god's words to the dead. Understanding his defeat, Vafthrudnir gave himself up to death.

Thus, according to Norse accounts, the god Odin, father of both gods and men, took from the elder race its secret wisdoms, thereby strengthening his own kind and setting in motion the giants' long decline. And it is true that as centuries passed and the human children of the gods spread their nets of civilization across the earth, the giants were seldom seen. Yet the race did not wholly die, and the wise and benevolent aspect of its character did not wholly disappear, as various accounts from later ages show.

Most of these tales, like that of the giant of Grabbist, speak of giants who lived alone and entered only briefly into the affairs of humankind. Sometimes they gave humans the gift of knowledge. On the fringes of Switzerland, for instance, it was said that the men and women who knew how to heal with herbs gained their lore from giants. In the Tyrol, the secrets of making cheese and butter were thought to be giants' wisdom, gladly given.

Sometimes giants were the bestowers of plenty and the guardians of fecundity. Thus, in Carinthia—a province in Austria rich in wheat and rye and covered with orchards — elusive mountain giants called wild men watched over the crops and ensured good harvests. The forests of Bohemia sheltered a giantess named Mordion, who aided women in childbirth, appearing during the dark hours to ease the women's pain and bring new children into the world, then disappearing as quietly as she had come.

Often the giants' offerings to humans were in proportion to their own immense size. Farmers in the Swedish province of Dalsland, close to the Norwegian border, described a year in which the giants came down from the high country into the farmers' hayfields to graze their cattle — or so it seemed on summer mornings, when the fields were found shorn and flattened by enormous hoofs. Throughout the summer and autumn of that year, the farmers complained about this, and they worried that the health of their own cattle would suffer from lack of feed during the winter. But the giants made restitution: The farmers discovered that each load of hay brought in during the autumn had tripled in size by Christmastide. This, they said, was giants' magic. In Zealand, the principal Danish island bordering the Baltic Sea, similar tales were told of giants who borrowed housewives' home-brewed ale, returning good ale in a quantity seven times greater than what they had borrowed.

In Iceland, fishermen whispered of giants and giant ogres — called trolls — that ruled the barren hills and untrod mountains. These old beings filled humans with terror, yet even they could serve as protectors. During an especially bleak winter, for example, one small fishing settlement be-came ice-locked, so that the men could not take their boats out. Soon the villagers began to starve. The children weakened and wailed with hunger; the adults sank into despair. But their plight was observed, it seemed. One day, the people saw a form swaying on a nearby mountain crest, as if a part of the earth itself had come to life. It was a giant troll wife, and she spoke words that rang in the air:

Mighty ones!" she cried. "Mighty ones, save these people. Let a great fish come willingly to them." The giantess was calling on her own gods, or perhaps she simply spoke to the sea. In any case, her plea was answered. In the morning, a great whale lay dying on the ice of the town's little harbor. Its flesh and blood and blubber provided the villagers with food and fuel until the confining ice thawed and broke apart in the spring. They never saw the giantess again, but her kindness was never forgotten.

Most tales of beneficent giants are vignettes such as these. There remained, however, a very few stories of giants who had more than merely glancing contact with mortals — giants who were kings of whole nations, heroes, teachers and fathers to their people.

Some of these tales came from Armenia, on the Black Sea, a country that, from earliest times, was a battleground for invaders — first Assyrians, then Persians, then Greeks, Romans, Huns and Arabs. More than most people, the Armenians had need of strong protectors. Their first leader and hero was Hayk, a beautiful colossus — said

Scion of the sea, the giant Bran the Blessed ruled the island of Britain in early days. It was he, sitting in state on the cliffs of Wales and gazing far across the water, who first sighted the sails of the King of Ireland, approaching on a fateful embassy.

to be a descendant of Noah – who led the Armenian tribes north from Babylonia to their mountain home. From him the Armenians took their first name: They called themselves the Hay and their land Hayastan. In Christian times, the people were led by David of Sassoun, a giant and the son of a giant, who for many decades fought off the invading caliphs of Egypt and Persia. Stories about him portray a rollicking hero, an exuberant warrior of gigantic appetites and ferocious temper. In his old age, he found that his son, a giant himself, had become superior in strength. During a quarrel with the youth, David cursed him with sterility, thereby ending the line of giants who ruled in Armenia. As for David, he died by the hand of his daughter, the offspring of a sorceress he had seduced and abandoned. The girl shot him with a poisoned arrow when she found him bathing in a stream.

On a loftier plane was the story of the ancient guardian King of Britain, a giant who watched over his people even after death. He was Bendigeidfran, or "Bran the Blessed," and he, more than other giants of his age, seemed still to have some essence of the elder gods in him. Bran lived in the era of the Celts. He was the son of a Princess named Penarddun, daughter of Beli – that is, of the earliest Welsh ruler—and through her inherited his throne. He had a sister, Branwen—a woman of normal size and surpassing beauty—and a brother, Manawyddan, who was also of human height. These three were called the Children of Llyr, for their father was thought to be a god of the sea—*llyr* in Welsh—or perhaps even the sea itself. By a mortal man, Penarddun had also had two other offspring, twins whose names were Nissyen and Evnissyen.

One fine spring morning Bran sat outside the wood and stone ramparts of his fortress at Harlech, on the northwest coast of Wales, taking counsel with his brother Manawyddan in the open air. This was his custom, for no hall was large enough to contain Bran. For a while, the men's half-brothers, the twin sons of Penarddun, spoke with them. Evnissyen was a spiteful man, sick with self-love and ever alert for a slight or quarrel. Evidently he found it that day, for he left the King's company in a rage and rode away to his own lands. With a sigh, his brother Nissyen asked the King's leave and followed Evnissyen, hoping to calm him.

Bran made no comment on the ugly incident. He was used to the temper of Evnissyen and noticed it little more than he would the sting of a fly. He simply continued his conversation with Manawyddan and the lords of his council, all the while keeping his farsighted eyes on something the others could not see: the white sails of unknown ships that were approaching from the west. The sails were much closer in by the time ordinary eyes discerned them and the alarm went up from the fortress (few sights were less welcome in those days than the unannounced appearance of a fleet of warships). Bran remained unperturbed throughout the blowing of the battle horns and the shouts of his warriors. He had seen the inverted shield that was slung from the bow of the leading ship, a sign that the strangers came in peace. Calling for silence, he ordered heralds down to the strand to parley with the visitors before they touched the shore.

The fleet, it turned out, was an embassy, led by Matholwch, King of Ireland. He sought alliance with Bran, and as a sign of union he wanted the hand of Branwen, daughter of Llyr.

There was a stir among Bran's men at this. Daughter of the sea, Branwen bore the title of Chief Ancestress of Britain. She was the treasure of the Island of the Mighty, as Britain was called, and her person had something of the sanctity of her giant brother's. But Bran reflected only a short time before he replied.

"This seems a good thing," he said to his men. Then he spoke across the water to the Irish: "Welcome to this island, lord. Come ashore and let us take counsel with you."

The ships were beached then. While the Irish warriors made the vessels fast and slid wooden ramps down onto the sand, Matholwch the King leaped lightly to shore. He was a man, not a giant, but he was magnificent—tall and straight, with chestnut hair and a merry face. His cloak was pinned with a brooch of silver and amber. Around his neck was a twisted torque of gold, such as only kings might wear. Throwing his head back, he squinted upward, surveying Bran and the ramparts of Bran's fortress, while behind him, their bridles clinking with rows of enameled ornaments, the glossy horses of the Irish pranced down ramps onto the sand.

This clearly was a fine match for Branwen, the flower of Britain, and all could see it. Although there was some talk in Bran's council that night of the danger of letting the maid leave her island and live among strangers, Matholwch's demeanor was so kind and his speech so generous that Bran, Manawyddan and others of the ruling circle were convinced of his honor. And there could be no doubting the practical advantages of the marriage treaty: By uniting British and Irish, it would make both strong. The match was therefore arranged. Branwen, when she saw the shining King who had sailed the sea to find her, said that she was pleased.

The formalities were performed with dispatch. Bran traveled north with his sister and his court, riding overland and across the Menai Strait to the island now called Anglesey, but once known as Môn, Mam Cymru, or the "Mother of Wales." This island was a holy place—a sanctuary for British priests, the principal seat of British Kings and the burial ground for British chieftains. Under Anglesey's rolling fields wound the many-chambered tombs of Kings so ancient that even their names had been forgotten.

The Irish, traveling by sea, met the British company on the island, and there they feasted with Bran and his brother Manawyddan. Then the royal pair was bedded. Branwen thus became Queen of Ireland, and the maid of Britain no more.

Bran's half-brother Evnissyen was the only British lord not present, for he had remained sulking in seclusion on his own lands. He came to Anglesey soon enough, however, when rumors of great doings reached him. Being a devious man, he did not greet the Kings or enter their tents. On the night he arrived, he drifted to the meadows where the Irish horses were penned. There he chatted with the horse guards and learned that his half-sister had been given to the Irish King and a treaty made with Ireland—and all this without his being consulted.

Evnissyen had not been given his due. Now he had a real grievance, and fury took hold of him. Without thought, he gave himself to his pleasure, which was anger and pain. He killed the men who guarded the horses. Then, with his jeweled knife, he fell upon the animals. According to the chronicles, he maimed them, "cutting their lips to the teeth, their ears down to the head, and their tails to the rumps, and where he could get a grip on them, he cut their eyelids to the bone."

The screams of the animals roused the camp and brought both Irish and British running to the bloodied meadow, where Evnissyen now stood panting, his knife still in his hand and a smile of mad triumph playing about his mouth. His people seized him and led him away. To prevent battle on the spot, Bran and Matholwch summoned their warriors and retired to their separate tents, leaving a few men to put the mutilated horses out of pain.

Matholwch spoke not a word to his wife. He ordered one of his men to lead her across the field to Bran's tent. When Branwen tried to question the man, he turned his head away. He could not speak to the British woman, for the torture of horses was a sacrilege so terrible that its stain would linger for centuries.

The Celts – Irish and British alike – were famed for their horsemanship, and the powers of their cavalry were renowned. But the horse was far more than a mount to them. It partook of divinity; it was an animal of the life-giving sun. Throughout the Celtic lands, the image of the horse was to be found stamped on coins, cast in bronze to make little votive objects, carved in giant scale on hillsides. Sometimes the gods of the Celts manifested themselves as horses; the goddess of fertility was named Epona, or "Divine Horse."

So charged with elemental power was the animal that, unlike other beasts, it seems not to have been used in sacrifice except on the greatest occasions. It was not, for instance, buried as a companion to the dead. But as late as the 12th Century, according to the churchman and traveler Gerald of Wales, tribes in the north of Ireland, who thought themselves descendants of horses, anointed their Kings by means of a curious ritual. The King apparent of the region publicly mated with a white mare, thereby espousing his kingdom, to which the mare held sovereignty, and ensuring its fertility.

Then the beast was sacrificed and its flesh cooked to make a broth that the King bathed in and drank.

Every man and woman on Anglesey that night knew the evil that Evnissyen had done. In the Irish camp, Matholwch and his men prepared to leave the desecrated place and return to their own lands. But a message from Bran stopped them. In a few simple words, the British King said that he himself had been as dishonored by Evnissyen's deed as the Irish and that he would make compensation. He could not incur the bloodguilt of killing Evnissyen, the son of his own mother. But he offered Matholwch a horse for every horse that had died. And he promised more – a measure of silver as thick as Matholwch's finger and a plate of gold as large as his head.

Finally, Bran said that he would give a treasure greater than all of these things, one that would protect the land of Ireland. It was giant's work from the oldest times – a caldron that could restore life. If a dead warrior was thrown into this vessel, he would rise and fight again, although he would have neither soul nor speech.

This was an honor price indeed – a magic to replace the magic that had died with the horses. Matholwch took it. He welcomed Branwen back to his bed; he stayed to feast with Bran and to receive the British horses that were brought. He gave orders to his company that none was to speak of the affair of the horses. Shortly thereafter, he sailed for Ireland with his thirteen ships, carrying Branwen with him.

Branwen's years in Ireland were good

To unite the islands of Ireland and Britain, Bran tendered to the Irish King his sister Branwen, of fair human form and sacred heritage. As the companies of the two Kings celebrated, however, a villain plotted against them both.

ones at first. The Irish welcomed her as Queen. Within Matholwch's fortress, they built her a sunny chamber such as great ladies had then, a little house filled with light and thatched with feathers from bright-colored birds. They smiled and murmured when she passed through the hall in her fleecy cloak and silken, gold-embroidered tunic, and they took with pleasure the gifts she gave, for Branwen was as openhearted and generous as she was beautiful. The chroniclers wrote, "No great lord or lady in Ireland would come to see Branwen to whom she did not give a brooch or ring or precious gem that would be remarkable to see given away." In that first year, too, she bore a healthy son to Matholwch. The boy was named Gwern, and Branwen loved him dearly.

But sadness followed the daughter of Llyr. In the second year of her marriage, it seems, Matholwch's warriors talked. Before long, the tale of the slaughter of the King's horses and of his dishonor at British hands spread throughout the court, and Matholwch's people began to call for revenge. The object of vengeance they chose was the obvious one – the British woman who had become their Queen. They demanded that Matholwch put Branwen away from him. Matholwch was fond of his wife, but he was a frail reed that bent before every wind. He summoned Branwen to his hall and, as his people looked on, told her that she would have to bear the punishment for her half-brother's deed. She was not to be conveyed home, for her disgrace might rouse the British to arms. Instead, she was consigned to Matholwch's kitchens, to work among the slaves.

"You have put me away before, lord, and took me again when the honor price was paid," Branwen said.

Matholwch did not reply.

"And what of my son?" she asked the King. He glanced at the people in the hall.

"He is Ireland's son, not yours," Matholwch replied. "He will be put into fosterage with a great Irish lord."

"You are a weakling, Matholwch," said Branwen. She turned without another word and walked from the hall. Mutterings about outlanders followed her. Someone spat contemptuously.

Thus began years of darkness. Branwen saw nothing of Matholwch or of his courtiers or of her son. She labored in the dirt-floored house of the King's kitchen, performing the work of the humblest scullions – skinning animals before they were dressed, turning the spits over the fires that cooked them. After some months, the Irish slaves ignored her, since she never answered their jibes and taunts. Each day, as a kind of ritual, the butcher gave her a slap on the ear, but after the first day, when tears stung her eyes and the butcher laughed, Branwen ignored him, too. She stared directly at him

When the Irish King left Britain, he carried a treasure, given as an honor price for the wrong that was done him. It was a charmed caldron that restored life to the dead.

and took the blow without flinching, then turned back to her work.

Among Branwen's tasks was the kneading of dough, and it presented her with some small companionship. A starling chick appeared one day at her kneading trough. Too small as yet to fly, the bird would have died but for Branwen, who fed it scraps of meat from the butchering. The chroniclers recorded that she instructed the bird in human speech. One evening, she held it to her ear to hear it recite the words she had taught it. "Hail, Bran the Blessed, son of Llyr," the starling said in its tiny voice. "May you prosper. Branwen, daughter of Llyr, sends greetings and asks for freedom from the prison Matholwch made for her and vengeance for the honor she has lost." When the little speech was ended, Branwen tucked a tiny scroll of silk, saved from her happy days, into the bird's beak to serve as a token. Then she raised her

hand at the open door of the kitchen and launched the starling into the air. The last she saw of it was the light on its wing as it flew before the wind, heading east toward Wales.

Months passed with no change in the dreary round of work. Branwen skinned the animals, turned the spits, kneaded the dough and took the butcher's daily blow.

One afternoon, however, the kitchen slaves began to chatter and busy themselves near Branwen's kneading trough.

Matholwch the King was coming. He stooped to enter the kitchen, his head grazing the smoke-blackened beams. Two men were with him. With a wave of his hand, Matholwch sent the kitchen slaves scurrying from the room. Then he spoke to the wife he had not seen in three years.

"Greetings, lady," he said. "These men tell of something strange upon the eastern sea. Hear what they have to say, and explain the meaning of it, if you can."

"No lady now, Matholwch," said Branwen dryly. And indeed, she was gaunt and pale from her hours in the darkened kitchen. Her woolen tunic was ragged and stained with blood and kitchen filth. But her gesture to her husband's minions had the same grace and courtesy she had shown as Queen.

The men said that they had seen a wonder on the sea. Over the waters to the east, a forest moved, and in the center of this forest was a moving mountain. Music, they said, floated across the sea to shore.

Branwen smiled at last, a wintry smile. "The forest trees are the masts and yardarms of the ships of Britain. The mountain is my brother Bran the Blessed, son of Llyr. The music comes from the trumpeter he carries on his shoulder, and it sounds the call to war. No ship will hold Bran, and so he wades the ocean with his men to rescue me from Matholwch."

"What shall I do?" cried Matholwch.

"If you want a man left alive in Ireland, you will treat with him, not fight him," Branwen said. She turned her back and bent to her kneading trough. The sight of Matholwch, whom she had loved, now sickened her.

It was said by the chroniclers that the Irish tried one ploy before they surrendered to Bran: They burned the bridge that spanned the Liffey River. They expected that this would slow or even check the advance of the Britons, but the river was no barrier to Bran the Blessed. He lay down across it, stretching his great body from bank to bank. Then his warriors in their thousands marched across his back.

They made camp on the riverbank, and that night they gathered in council. In the morning, Matholwch sent messengers to Bran. The Irish King offered to surrender his sovereignty to Branwen's son, Gwern.

Bran looked down at the messengers with contempt. "That is not enough honor price for the pain of my sister," he said. "Find some better recompense, and I will speak with you once more before the killing starts."

The messengers were back the next day with another offer. As before, Bran was told that Gwern could have the Irish kingship. Branwen would be restored to her brother, and a mighty house would be built in Bran's honor on the plain by the river. In this house, a feast of peace would be held between British and Irish, and Matholwch would pay Bran homage.

Bran spoke with his brothers. Then he agreed to the terms, for they came from Branwen. She had made them to save bloodshed in Ireland.

Within an hour, Branwen rode from the Irish King's fortress to the encampment of her brother. Matholwch rode beside her, speaking urgently, but she never glanced at him. She attended only to her son, who sat in front of her on her palfrey, his small hands wound in the horse's mane. At the border of the British camp stood Bran, taller than the trees; without a word he bent and plucked the woman and boy from the saddle and carried them to his fire. Math-

Tutored in human speech by Branwen, a starling braved the winds and distances of the Irish Sea to bear home to Bran the tale of her husband's cruelty.

Watchmen wove a riddle for the King of Ireland: Off the coast, a mountain moved; in its wake a forest crept. Branwen gave the answer: The trees were ships' masts, the mountain her brother, wading the seas to free her.

olwch raised his hand in farewell, but he had no answering wave from his wife.

Branwen mentioned her time in Ireland just once, to tell her brothers how Matholwch had used her. At the end of her account, Manawyddan said angrily, "This is Evnissyen's doing. It was his deed that brought grief upon our sister."

Above their heads, Bran's deep voice commanded silence. Evnissyen did not reply to Manawyddan's bitter words, but his lips were tight, and his eyes glittered with his old rage.

For the most part, however, the weeks in camp passed peacefully. The Irish hewed trees and wove thatch to make a many-columned hall for Bran on the plain below the Irish fortress. The British talked of home; their harpers sang, and Branwen sang with them in her pretty voice. Her son ran freely among the soldiers, and at night he slept under the stars with Bran, curling his small body between the giant's neck and shoulders in the depths of his warm beard.

At last, the hall was ready. Its thatch seemed to graze the clouds, and its tree-columns were painted in the red and gold the Irish loved. On the afternoon before the house was consecrated and the feasting began, Evnissyen went into the hall to inspect its arrangements. He walked through the echoing chamber with an Irish warrior beside him for escort. The hall was thick with shadow. A shaft of sunlight from the smokehole in the ceiling struck a painted column and attracted Evnissyen's quick eye. From pegs on either side of the column hung bulging sacks made of hide.

"What is this?" said Evnissyen.

"Grain, Brother, for the feasting," the Irishman replied.

"Is it so?" said Evnissyen. He ran his fingers over the bag. As he pressed the hide, it revealed the contours of a man and a spear shaft. He felt for the head, gripped it with both hands and pressed, straining mightily. A muffled groan sounded, bone cracked, and a stain of red spread slowly on the outside of the bag.

Then Evnissyen turned to the white-faced Irish warrior beside him and said, "Now we will visit every column." This they did. On each column, two hide sacks hung, encasing armed Irishmen. One by one, he crushed the men's heads between his powerful hands. At the end, when the blood-soaked bags had begun to drip onto the floor of the hall, he told his terrified escort, "Clear this filth out. And conceal no more Irishmen in this hall to prey upon the British." Then he left the place.

But Evnissyen said nothing of the treachery to his companions, and the British and Irish feasted in the hall that night. Their benches were arranged in rows on either side of the blazing hearth. On one side, his head towering near the roof beams, sat Bran, with Branwen beside him and the boy Gwern standing at her knee. Manawyddan was there, and Nissyen and Evnissyen. Across the flames stared Matholwch and the Irish. Matholwch had no word to say when the kingdom was given to Branwen's son and all his warriors swore fealty to the boy.

After that, the drinking horns passed freely among the company. The Irish sang praises of their little King; the British sang praises of Branwen. The child Gwern trotted easily among his uncles, Bran and Manawyddan and Nissyen, until Evnissyen said sharply, "Why does the boy not come to me? I would love him even if he were not King of Ireland."

Hearing the harshness in the words, the child turned uncertainly toward his mother. But Branwen, feeling safe among her brothers and at peace with the world, nodded. Gwern went to Evnissyen's arms.

The moment that followed was etched forever in the mind of every person there. Evnissyen, lover of strife, lifted the little boy high in the air and hurled him headfirst into the hearth fire. His skull shattered on the logs before he could cry out.

The cry that tore the air was the scream of Branwen. She lurched toward the fire, intent on dying with her son. Bran interceded, grasping her with one hand while he fumbled for his spear with the other.

Chaos erupted in the hall. The Irish threw themselves against the British, intent on avenging their child-king. Howling their battle cries, warriors hacked and slashed, until the floor of the hall was slippery with blood and littered with the bodies of the dead and dying.

The foes were evenly matched at first. The British held their adversaries off, and Bran, alone in one corner, killed every warrior who approached, keeping Branwen safe. Then Evnissyen, fighting by the entry to the hall, saw a frightening thing: a blackened, blank-eyed warrior, as stiff as a puppet but deadly in his efficiency, swinging a battle-ax among the British. Heads bounced from his blade, and

After suing for peace, the Irish conceived a cunning treachery. They built a feasting hall for Bran, then hid warriors in sacks they said were full of grain. Bran's kinsman saw the ruse and crushed each warrior's skull.

British and Irish fought in the feasting hall, and the Irish met might with magic,
reviving slain warriors in the charmed caldron. But no Irish spear pierced Bran's
great shield or harmed Branwen where she sheltered in its arc.

fountains of blood arched around him.

"A dead man fights," cried Evnissyen, and forced his way to the door. Outside, a fire blazed, and on it smoked the caldron that Bran had given Matholwch as an honor price for Evnissyen's slaughter of the Irish horses. Around the caldron the Irish dead were heaped, and from its mouth crawled bodies quickened by its magic. They came swiftly, so many black spiders, their eyes empty, their mouths loose. They swarmed past Evnissyen, and in the hall they killed and killed.

Faced with both the living and the dead, the British were doomed. Evnissyen knew it. The death of his own race was on his head. He knew that, too. Remorse, or perhaps the simple need that his own kind should survive, acted upon him then and overcame the hate that had always ruled him. He threw himself into the pile of Irish corpses, then feigned death. In time he was picked up by a warrior who worked among the dead. Mistaking the Briton for one of his own people, the warrior heaved Evnissyen into the caldron of regeneration. There, amid the twitching corpses, Evnissyen lay. He stretched his arms and legs wide, pressing against the caldron sides, and called upon his gods. He was a man of prodigious strength, but the power of his limbs was now multiplied many times over. With a roar, the vessel burst asunder. Evnissyen's

heart burst, too, but he had saved his people, for the Irish could no longer bring their dead to life. Thus Evnissyen was long remembered, not only for the evil of his life, but for the act that redeemed it.

The chroniclers say that the battle raged on for many days and that the slaughter was terrible. In the end, according to the tale, all that remained of the Irish race was five pregnant women, hiding in caves. Of the British who had come to Ireland, there were only Branwen and Bran the Blessed, and seven men whose names were given as Pryderi; Manawyddan; Glifieu Eil Taran; Taliesin; Ynawg; Grudyeu, son of Muriel; and Heilyn, son of Gwyn Hen.

Bran had been wounded in the heel by a poisoned spear, and his end was near. Lying where he had fallen, he told his companions what they must do and what was to come. They were to strike off his head, he said, and carry it home to Britain. A time of rest then would be given to them. When it was over, they were to bury the head in London beneath Gwynfryn—that is, "the white mount." The head would serve as a protector of the country. They did as Bran said. They struck off

Bran the Blessed died in Ireland. His severed head—still charged with ancient power—
was carried home to Britain and buried there to guard against all the island's enemies.

his noble head and carried it home. When they landed, Branwen's heart broke at last, because of her grief for herself and for all those who had died. The warriors buried her by the shore and went on to the island of Gwales off the south coast of the country. There, in a castle high above the sea, the tale says, the company of warriors spent many years. During this time the head of Bran was with them. It spoke to them and guided them, so that they came to be called the Assembly of the Noble Head. The birds of Rhiannon, Queen of the other world, were with them, too. These birds' song banished memory and care, so that the warriors had the ease of childhood for that period of resting.

The enchanted time ended at last, however, as Bran had said it would. Heilyn, son of Gwyn Hen, one day opened a forbidden door

of the castle on Gwales. He looked out east across Britain from that door, and as he looked, memory and grief came flooding back—and also the knowledge that the life of his country must go on. Then the company carried the giant's head to London and buried it, as they had been bidden, with its face toward France. For centuries, Bran the Blessed rested under the white mount, brooding silently over Britain and the British, and in all the long years of his watching, no enemy harmed the people he guarded.

As King Arthur's courtiers celebrated Christmastide, a giant stranger rode into the banqueting hall.

The Tests of the Green Knight

Many giants cared nothing for mortal affairs, but some watched the world of men with ancient, laughing eyes, and when the time was right, these spell-wreathed beings came forth to test the younger race. Such a giant lived in Britain once, and at the court of King Arthur he tried the mettle of the finest of Arthur's knights.

The adventure began in midwinter, in the magic hours at the turn of the year. That was a time of revelry in Arthur's court, when hearths blazed high and pipes and lutes sang loud. Filled with merriment, the King cried that he would not feast until he had heard a tale of marvels or seen a stranger challenge his own champions.

Such demands were a midwinter custom, but the King got an answer he had not bargained for. An icy wind swept into the hall, bringing a stranger like none ever met before. The newcomer was a giant astride a mighty stallion. Despite the winter dark outside the castle walls, he was clothed in summer colors. His silks were the green of meadow grass; his horse was caparisoned in sea green silk and shod with emerald. In one hand, the giant bore a branch of holly, green with life in the midst of the dead season; in the other, he held a curving battle-ax. Silence fell. Green was the hue of Faerie, the magi-

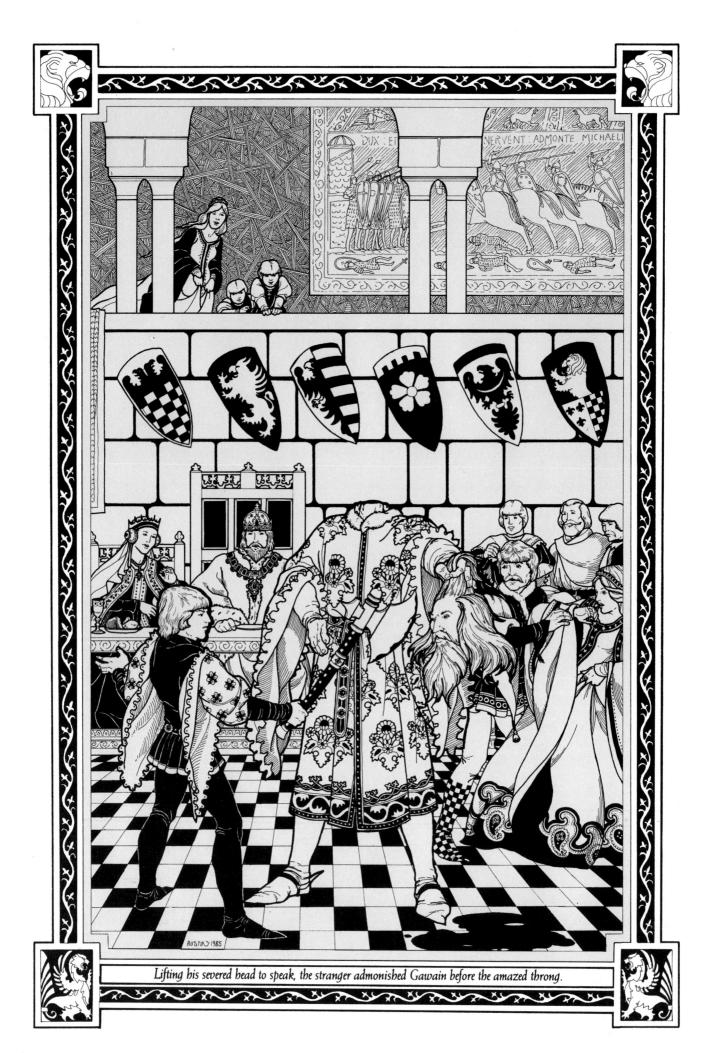

Lifting his severed head to speak, the stranger admonished Gawain before the amazed throng.

cal kingdom that lay beyond the reach of mortal sight.

The Green Knight spoke like a man, however. He called this challenge to the King's high table: that one warrior should behead him with his own battle-ax, and that, after a year and a day had passed, the warrior should willingly take the same blow in return.

"This is folly," said the King, but he moved to take the challenge. He was forestalled. Bright-haired Gawain sprang forward. Gawain was the greatest of Arthur's company then, perfect in valor and in truth and honor. To stand as champion was all his desire. Knowing this, Arthur assented to his plea, and so the Green Knight and Gawain made their pact. The Green Knight dismounted. He gave his ax to Gawain; he knelt to take the blow.

With the speed and grace of youth, Gawain swung the ax. It whistled in the air and bit through the giant's neck, so that the head thudded to the floor, spilling scarlet on the paving stones. Then, while the courtiers stared, the mighty body rose. In one hand it lifted its severed head and turned the face toward Gawain. The mouth moved.

"Remember your word, young knight," it said. "In a year and a day you shall come to me at the Green Chapel in the northern lands." Then, with a long, rolling laugh, the knight mounted and, holding his bleeding head aloft, rode alone into the dark.

The King broke the silence that followed this scene. He called for wine and so brought back the gaiety of the winter feast. Gawain, too, was merry: It would have been unseemly to comment on his valiant bargain, whose end, after all, was a year away.

But that year passed as swiftly as a sigh. The winter flowered into spring, and summer came, golden with

The chill mists lifted to reveal a shining castle above the trees, beckoning the weary traveler.

grain and fragrant with fruit. Summer died, as it was bound to, and when the last apple had fallen from the tree, Gawain set out alone, riding northward over fields of frosted stubble. He made a shining figure, for he was armored in gold. On his crimson shield was engraved a pentangle, a five-pointed star made of overlapping lines that served in those days as an emblem of truth.

The way was hard and the winds were cold. Snow swirled around the solitary rider and mantled the ground beneath his horse's hoofs. Day after day he rode through wasteland, climbing at last into the mountains of the north. What few people he saw were poor and frightened. They shook their heads when Gawain asked about the Green Chapel and its knight.

He spent nights in the open, huddling close to a wind-blown fire. Finally, on a day of stinging snow, Gawain found shelter. In the afternoon, a mist rose from the ground, barring his way. He halted, but a light winked through the wall of cloud and the mist melted, revealing in a mountain cleft ahead the gilded turrets of a castle. Gawain spurred forward, eager for rest and company.

He was received by the lord of the place, a bluff and ruddy knight, huge and thickly muscled. His name was Bercilak. He heard the wanderer's tale with the interest of a fellow warrior and, in the end, nodded briskly.

"I know the Green Chapel, and I will have you taken to the place when the time is nigh," he said. Then he signaled for music, and Gawain was drawn into the warmth of Bercilak's winter feast.

They spoke no more of the Green Knight, but later, when the fires sank low and the wine passed freely, Bercilak said with a smile, "Let us make a winter bargain to match your first, young knight. Rest here for your or-

The lady sighed sweetly, and she pressed upon Gawain a sash that would shield him from harm.

deal. My wife will care for your comfort. I will hunt tomorrow, and what I find, I will give to you. What you chance on here, you will give to me."

"Done," said Gawain. "I like your eye for sport."

But he liked it less in the morning, when he lay alone in a tower chamber, listening to the winding of the hunting horns outside. His door swung silently open, and Bercilak's wife glided into the room, her silks rustling on the floor. She was as pretty in the morning light as she had seemed at the feasting. But she wanted more than his admiration: She made clear that she desired Gawain.

To accede would have been a betrayal of his host and of his honor. Gawain put the lady off with banter, and at length she left him. In farewell, she leaned so close that he could smell her flowery summer scent, and she kissed him gently. Then she swept from the room.

In the afternoon, Bercilak returned bearing a deer, which he said was to be Gawain's. True to the bargain he had made, Gawain kissed his host on the cheek in return, for he had been given a kiss that day. Bercilak glanced at his wife. Then he shrugged and laughed.

A second night passed in the same way as the first, and a second morning, and a second afternoon, when Gawain gave Bercilak his lady's kiss. As before, the older knight merely laughed. On the third morning, however, while Bercilak hunted, the lady came again to Gawain, and this time she was sad. She said that if Gawain would not have her love, he must take a token of it. From her narrow waist she unwound a length of green silk shot with gold. This was an enchanted girdle, she said. It protected the wearer from harm.

And Gawain thought of the Green Knight's blade and of the fountain that rose from the headless neck and of

His trial of honor and courage concluded, Gawain received the ancient giant's blessing.

the Green Chapel. He took the magic girdle. He did not give it to Bercilak when the lord returned from hunting.

The fourth morning was the time of his ordeal. Gawain rose in darkness. A squire sent by Bercilak helped him into his golden armor and tied the silken girdle. The boy guided him through twisting paths toward what he said was the place of the chapel. He left Gawain near it.

There was no chapel—only a tangle of fir trees, a natural sanctuary walled by icy cliffs and roofed by snow-laden boughs. Here the Green Knight waited. On legs as thick as tree trunks he loomed above Gawain's head, his own head on his shoulders and his great ax gleaming.

Brave Gawain knelt in the snow, as he had promised. The Green Knight swung three times. At the first swing, Gawain jerked his head aside and out of the scything path of the blade. The giant sneered. At the second, it was the giant who stayed the ax. The final swing swerved wide, nicking at Gawain's neck. His blood flowered in the snow, but the bargain with the Green Knight was complete and Gawain lived. He leaped to his feet, prepared to fight.

The Green Knight merely leaned on his ax handle and smiled and spoke in Bercilak's voice. "Well done, Sir Gawain," said he. "The first two blows I feinted: These were for the days you resisted my wife's temptations and honestly gave me what you got. The third blow was for your failure: You took my lady's girdle because you loved your life and feared my ax. It is a small flaw only, and your courage makes amends for it."

Then the giant of disguises and of temptations turned away. Gawain saw him no more. But he wore the green talisman for the rest of his days, to remind him of his failure at the giant's test.

Chapter Three

A Deepening Enmity

Life in Lapland—that vast wilderness stretching across the top of Scandinavia—long had a changeless quality. Summer after brief, bright summer, Laplanders in hide boots, many-peaked embroidered caps and coats of red and blue let their reindeer herds roam free in the mountains of the western coast; each year when a chill returned to the land, they gathered the animals in and drove them east to the bog-laced plateau—called the *vidda* by the Norwegians—where the herds and their guardians settled in for the season of darkness.

In the old days, the Lapps rarely ventured north toward the Arctic coast: They were hardy people, but all knew of the land in the north called Trollebotn, or Troll Bottom, a wind-swept waste haunted by huge, murderous beings. No Laplander cared to face those trolls, some of them three-headed, some with more hideous deformities, all malevolent and filled with hatred for humankind. But a Lapp woman and her son once were forced to cross the boundaries into trolls' territory. This is their tale:

The woman, called Mari, was the wife of a rich herder. Her journey began in the rolling highlands at dusk one September day, just after the time when the herds were gathered in. At that season, mists hung all day over the mountain lakes, the birch forests flamed into autumnal gold, and long skeins of geese and ducks trailed southward across the pale skies. Already the afternoons were drawing in.

This year was not like others, however. Mari had seen strange shadows in the twilit afternoons, and they frightened her. She had protested when her son Nils left to hunt alone before the family's journey east; she watched every evening from the house, her fingers plucking nervously at the logs, while her husband headed out toward the trees to milk his reindeer does. And because she watched, she saw him die. A massive figure leaped upon him from the trees and knocked him to the ground. A knife of bone flashed up and down in rhythmic arcs, spattering blood in the air. No sound came from Mari's husband: He twitched under the knife thrusts and then was still. When his movements ceased, the creature that had killed him —a giant troll—turned toward Mari, who stood paralyzed in the door of her house.

The troll's form was roughly that of a man, but it was twice a man's height. Over hunched shoulders, its white head gleamed bare. From its forehead protruded a stiff, curving horn of flesh; from its gaping mouth grew large and fanglike teeth.

The troll shambled toward her with a curious, lopsided gait, the dagger in one of its hands. But it did not stab her. It raised its free hand to strike, and that was the last thing Mari saw for a long while.

When consciousness returned, she found herself trussed and slung over the troll's shoulder. The creature was striding over rough ground toward the north, as Mari could tell from the direction of the last remaining daylight.

How far she traveled in this miserable fashion, she never afterward could tell. The ground passing beneath her eyes changed from leaf-littered forest floor to green bog to dry meadow to lichen-covered rock. The air grew steadily colder, and snow fell, first in large flakes, then in a shifting veil of white that blinded the woman and muffled the troll's footsteps.

The journey ended high in the mountains, at a hut half-buried in snow. Within its dark confines, the troll set Mari down and tethered her to a post by a length of thong; although she had some freedom of movement, her hands remained tied. The huge creature kindled its hearth fire, then squatted near the woman and surveyed her with dull, empty eyes.

"Pretty," it grunted. "Wife." It fumbled at her skirt with its four-fingered hand.

Mari replied in a faint but steady voice, "My son will follow us. When he finds you, he will kill you for murdering my husband and stealing me away."

The troll gave a bark of laughter and shook its head so that its horn quivered. In a groaning mumble, it chanted its power, explaining why such a mission of revenge was bound to fail. Its soul, said the troll, was hidden in an egg in a hen in a sheep in a cask on a fire-rimmed island of ice beyond the North Cape, and a body without a soul in it could not die. Only when the soul was slain would the troll perish, and no living mortal could find the soul.

The North Cape, jutting into the ice-choked Arctic Ocean, was far from the world of humankind, Mari knew. She leaned her head against the post and wept for her husband's death, for the son she would never see again, and for herself, trapped like an animal by a soulless thing that itself was even less than an animal.

While she wept, the troll remained squatting; it stared but made no further move to touch her. At last, it rose and shuffled to the door. "Food," it said, and trudged out into the blowing snow. She was left alone with the hiss and crackle of the fire on the hearth and her own sobs.

She quieted at once, however, when a low whistle echoed through the shadowy chamber. The next instant, the curtain of hide that served as a door moved. Mari's son—tall, strong, with a hunter's tautness about him—strode into the room. "Nils," she said with wonder.

"I followed the track," Nils said. "Now I will free you and we will leave this land. I carried skis for you." He set to work on Mari's bonds with his hunting knife.

It was useless, however. The knife slid off the thongs. Finally Nils gave up. "These are troll-made, and no human knife can cut them. I must kill the troll to set you free," he said.

His mother shook her head. Weeping once more, she told Nils how the troll had hidden its soul away. "Then I will find the creature's soul," said Nils matter-of-factly. He kissed his mother and was gone.

After a while, the troll returned, bearing a fat salmon it had caught. It paused in the entrance, swinging its heavy head from side to side and working its nostrils.

"Man smell," it said.

But Mari simply looked at the creature, and it turned its horned head away. Evidently it was uncomfortable under the direct gaze of a human. At length, it squatted and threw the fish onto the fire.

Weeks went by, and the ogre and Mari fell into a dismal routine. Each day the troll left the hovel and hunted, providing Mari at least the gift of solitude. Eventually, it returned with a fish or hare or other game, and this it roasted on its hearth. Then it fed her, stuffing the smoky meat into her mouth with its claws; never did it untie her hands so that she could feed herself. Each day it spent hours staring at its prize. Sometimes it fumbled at her clothing and said, "Pretty," and "Wife," but Mari found that it would back away if she fixed her eyes on its face.

The period of daylight grew ever shorter until, finally, the sun did not shine at all. Then the troll seemed to grow in strength, and even Mari's angry eyes were no defense: The troll pawed freely at her. At night it tightened her bonds and slept with its heavy body leaning against her, and its rank odor filled her nostrils. She ceased to look at it or listen to its clumsy speech; she simply endured.

One day, however, when the longest of winter's nights had passed, the troll's behavior changed. It lurched in its usual fashion to the door of the hut, but there it hesitated. With a guttural cry, it swung around on Mari and struck blindly at her. Its claw missed and cracked against the post. After that, the creature stood quite rigid, swaying. Its breath came and went in a horrible liquid wheezing, and black matter bubbled at its lips. At last, dropping to its knees, it crawled out into the snow.

A miracle followed: The thongs that bound Mari fell away. She crept to the door and peered out. The troll was lying on the ground, drooling its lifeblood onto the snow. A crack of returning daylight showed at the rim of the sky. She ran outside, but where was she to go in this unknown and frigid land? She could do nothing but huddle by the troll's hearth and wait for succor, while the troll itself lay beyond the door, its body shrouded by the drifting flakes.

Within days, help came: Nils returned to her, laughing with triumph and full of tales of enchantment. He had skied north toward the end of the world, he said, finally reaching a rocky cape that bordered a frozen sea. During his journey, he had not been alone. Many animals, strangely intelligent, lived in Trollebotn. Nils surmised that they had once been men, but trolls' magic had changed and bound them. In any event, they seemed to sense his mission and helped him on his way. A wolf carried him through rings of fire to the

In the snowy waste of troll country at the world's northern rim, a Lapp woman
named Mari fled her dying captor. Life drained from this horned troll
when a mortal man—Mari's son—found the hiding place of the monster's soul.

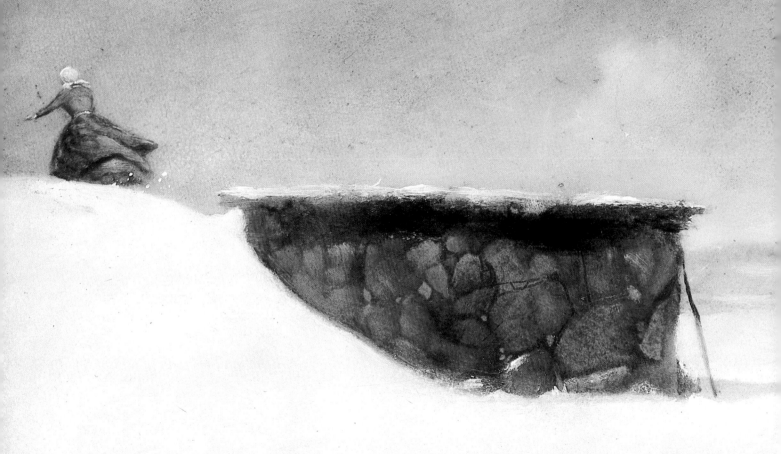

island of ice where the troll's soul was hidden in a sheep's body. The wolf tore the sheep apart, revealing the body of a hen. A hawk opened the hen, exposing the egg that sheltered the troll's soul. A heron caught the egg in its beak. Then, said Nils, he himself had smashed the egg. At that instant, the ring of fire died into the water around the island. The animals vanished, and three men stood in their places.

The moment when Nils crushed the egg was the same moment when, far from the ice island, the horned troll had staggered from its hut and died in the snow. It was the moment when Mari's bonds — no longer strengthened by troll magic — had fallen away, and when the first returning daylight had shown in the east. Mother and son marveled. Then they left Trollebotn, that place of evil magic, and took up life again among their own kind.

Such hostile enclaves as Trollebotn were the last fragments of the once-great kingdoms of giants and trolls. Generally located far from human habitation, they were no more than small pools left by the retreating tides of elder times, but they held great danger for humankind. There, the orderly laws of nature that men and women knew and trusted did not yet apply. The shapes and behavior of inanimate things were ever changing. The very trees of those lands might pull up their roots and dance in the moonlight to the giants' command, stately as human courtiers. In those old realms, animals could speak, sometimes because giants had magically endowed them with intelligence, and sometimes because they were human beings trapped by spells.

The giants themselves seemed to be tied to no corporeal form. Although their original guise appears to have been a stupendously outsized version of human shape, they could, if they chose, assume the form of a hawk for swiftness, a lion for ferocity, a serpent for venom.

They frequently did choose alternative bodies and all the other weaponry of magic, if the old tales speak true. Indeed, they did so more and more as time went on, and this was a sign of their decline. Their race — so majestic in the early days of the earth — was fading away as the vigor of humanity grew, and giants gave themselves up to fear and hatred. They became predators.

Why giants enchained some of their mortal enemies with spells is unclear; perhaps this exercise of power reassured them. But their range of cruelties was great. They stole human beings for slaves, as the Lapland troll had stolen the woman Mari. And they ate human flesh.

Not all who fell victim to the giants were caught on the home grounds of humanity. Humans occasionally ventured on their own into the terrain of ogres. This could easily happen by accident. The boundaries of giants' territories were as elusive and changeable as the giants themselves, who were sometimes visible and sometimes not, or — even more confusingly — visible to some men and women and not to others. Human senses were ill-equipped to deal with beings who could wield magic as effectively as these onetime rulers of the first world. If they desired, giants could live among humans

The fiery death of a Persian killer

Hidden in caves and pits amid the wilds of Persia lived the *afrīts*, demons of great size and loathsome habit, who preyed on mortals with weapons of magic. It was told of one such creature that he stole a maiden on the eve of her wedding and kept her for his own amusement, visiting her when the appetite seized him. At length, he killed her horribly, first cutting off her hands and feet, then striking off her head. As a final stroke of cruelty, he changed her human lover into an ape.

It took magic to defeat the power of the *afrīt*. A Princess skilled in sorcery recognized the ape for the human that he truly was; knowing the cause of the man's plight, she summoned the *afrīt* with chanted commands that he could not refuse. Then Princess and demon fought with spells. They fought in the shapes of lion and serpent, of eagle and wolf, of scorpion and vulture. At last they fought as flame, each of them wreathed in tongues of fire, and the Princess, calling aloud the name of her god, was the victor. The *afrīt* was burned to ashes.

At the demon's death, the man was restored to his rightful form. But the magical fire that had empowered the Princess was too great for a human body to endure. Her battle won, she expired in her own flame.

and never be seen. They could have kingdoms above the clouds. Their powers were past mortal understanding even in the days of the giants' decline.

Rumor might tell of places to avoid. Every Norse child had heard, for instance, that giant trolls laired under country bridges, preying on livestock, shepherds and farmers. As for Trollebotn, it was known to lie north of Lapland, although no one could say exactly where it began. The Lapps gave a wide berth to the northern mountains, assuming that trolls chose places large enough in scale to suit their size. The same wariness of mountains applied in other countries, and trackless forests were also regarded as unsafe.

The traveler who wandered into such regions might see no change in the terrain. In a forest, he might not discern the mighty legs that rose among the tree trunks or the eyes that peered down at him through the canopy of leaves. He would have no way of knowing that the wind among the branches was the sighing of the giant's breath, that the crack of distant thunder was the muttering of the watchful enemy. Only when fingers closed around his body, only when they jerked him into the air and he stared through a palisade of teeth into the glistening, crimson cavern of an eager mouth, would the hapless wayfarer realize that he had stepped across some boundary into the realm of the old ones. And that instant might be his last.

Sometimes it happened, however, that humans were given signs of the presence of giants. These might be objects that no human hand could master—a hunting knife long and broad enough to bridge a stream, or a gleaming needle that might serve a man as a sword. Or the warning would come in more subtle form: The things of nature would begin to behave unnaturally as a giant's magic quivered in the air.

A young Scots Prince had such an experience, and the story of his adventure is crowded with the inexplicable details common in tales of giants. In the course of a hunt, he found himself in a part of his own lands that he did not recognize. Before the day was out, he was forced to give a promise that would bring him years of grief.

The adventure began in a clearing in a forest bordering a deep loch, where the cold waters of the Atlantic Ocean pierced the Scottish coast. This clearing, strewn with golden leaves and warmed by the autumn sun, seemed quiet at first, and the young lord paused to rest for a while.

A hiss and a harsh cry broke the peace. From the wall of woods that surrounded the place hopped a raven, in the ugly, awkward manner peculiar to its kind. It gave its cry again but made no further move. Its eyes were fixed on a scattering of leaves; the bird seemed mesmerized. The Prince stood to investigate and found the reason for the raven's fear: A serpent lay coiled among the leaves. Its mottled black scales gleamed; its forked tongue delicately tasted the air; and its eyes were fastened on the bird. In a moment, it would strike.

Reacting quickly, the Prince struck the snake's head from its body with his sword. The bird, freed from its paralysis, cocked its head at him and gave its harsh cry once more. Then the air around the raven trembled. The bird's feathers swelled into shadow. From that shadow a youth emerged.

He was tall and handsome, dressed in the silks of some fine court and armed with a sword whose hilt glittered with jewels. He smiled at the tartan-clad hunter and made a graceful bow. "A thousand thanks, young lord," he said. "But for your kindness, I might have been trapped in raven form all my days. And those would certainly have been short."

He handed the Prince a sack that was made of fine, creamy wool and added, "This for the lifting of the enchantment. Open it only when you come to the place where you dwell." Without another word, the youth strode off into the trees.

The Prince should have been suspicious. He was on unfamiliar ground, and he had seen a transformation. In all likelihood, he was in giants' country. His best course would have been to leave the gift and head for home. Instead, he slung the bag over his shoulder and followed the path the stranger had taken.

The path led to a broad meadow. In its midst, he stopped to rest, setting the bag on the ground. Then curiosity overcame him. He opened the bag. The mouth fell back to reveal a miniature castle, somewhat like those that were made for little boys to play with, but more exquisitely perfect in detail than any toy could be. Every block of stone of every wall was sharp and clear, every turret was crowned with tiles of gold. Two tiny golden chains secured the drawbridge.

The Prince took the pretty thing in his hands and set it on the grass. At once, the little castle began to swell. Alarmed, he retreated to the edge of the clearing.

Skyward the towers soared. The walls pressed outward as each stone and mortar joint gained size. And as the building grew, leaves and then tree trunks shot up through the grass around it. Soon, a full-scale fortress stood before him, its turrets flying banners marked with his own family's device, its walls girdled with heavy-laden orchards.

The hunter saw a movement at a window and the white gleam of a face, but before he had time to consider it, something enormous took shape beside the castle. A giant was leaning comfortably on the outer wall and regarding the human before him. "This is giants' country, little man," he said. "You cannot build your fortress here and live."

The huntsman stiffened with fear, but he achieved a creditably intelligent reply. "I did not call forth this magic, giant, and it is a thing I cannot undo. I would take the building from your lands if I could."

"Oh, I can undo the magic," said the giant easily. "But I shall ask a price of you."

"And what is your price?"

"Your first-born son, when he reaches the age of seven."

The Prince had neither wife nor son; he therefore readily agreed to the price. With no further ado, the giant raised his hand to the keystone of the castle's gateway and pressed down, and at once the building began to dwindle, shrinking again to the size of a toy. Sliding it back into its woolen bag, he said, "Return to your own country. I will come for your son."

Matter was mercurial in giants' territory. The Scots said that in the hands of the old ones a mighty fortress might shrink to the size of a toy.

And that, the storytellers say, is what happened. The Prince retraced the path he had taken that day. He set the enchanted castle by a river, and it grew to its full splendor again – and within it was a woman to match, she whose face he had seen for a moment at the castle window. The huntsman married her.

For all the oddness of the circumstances, the marriage turned out to be a happy one. The Prince was content with his other-world wife, and she brought him good fortune, so that his fields were fertile and his people satisfied. She bore him a son, which gave the Prince both joy and fear, for he had not forgotten his pact. He said nothing of it to his wife. She had come into his world by magic, seemingly without memory of the time before the Prince had claimed her, and he did not want to frighten her.

When the boy reached his seventh year, however, she was frightened indeed. On the morning of the child's birthday, the giant's head and shoulders loomed above the walls of the castle suddenly, as if the creature had formed himself all at once from the empty air.

"Prince, I have come to claim my son," he said in a thundering voice.

Within the stronghold, the wife turned to her husband and cried out, "What is this?" And he had to tell her.

She refused to send her boy into the arms of the giant. Heedless of the Prince's protest, she had a cook's son dressed in the child's clothes and thrust forth in his place. From every window, the Prince's people watched the small child cross the castle courtyard. All saw the giant pick him up and whisper in his ear; all heard the treble reply, although the words could not be distinguished. And all saw how the giant then smashed the child against the castle's outer curtain wall so that the small head shattered on the stones.

"It is a mistake to trick me, Prince," said the giant. "Give me your son, or else every living thing within the fortress will die as the cook's son died." For emphasis, he smashed the castle gate with one huge fist as easily as a man might smash a toy.

The Prince had no choice. His wife wept piteously, but he sent his son out to the giant, a sacrifice of one for many. Boy and giant vanished together.

A long exile followed, and although the Prince's son escaped his prison at last, that was many years later, when the Prince was frail and dying and the boy had become a full-grown man, a stranger to his father.

Such were the perils of traffic with giants: The Scottish story did not unfold the mystery of the Prince's venture or tell whether the enchanted raven and the castle had been a giant's trick made to lure a mortal man. It told only that a human had wandered into giants' territory and, in the end, suffered for the transgression.

Yet, regardless of the danger, many such incursions were made intentionally, in the same way that the Laplander Nils tracked a troll to its lair. For all their puniness, humans could be redoubtable foes to giants, especially when fired by the desire to avenge depredations by the older race or to rescue fellow mortals.

The Irish had need for such mettle. Irish

Who knew where giants and their kind might dwell? Even shadows
under Scandinavian bridges provided lairs for livestock-hungry trolls.

chronicles tell of decades when the land was at the mercy of a being known as the giant of the Brown Beech Wood, a hate-filled spirit as tall as the trees (from which he seemed to derive his strength). Where exactly in Ireland his kingdom lay is no longer known, but most likely the place was in the chalky hills of Leinster, for the beech thrives on chalk.

In any case, an Irish King's son named Diarmuid penetrated the Brown Beech Wood once, picking his way around the great boles and over the silvery webs of roots. Finally, in a place where the leaves formed a canopy so dense that hardly any light leaked through, he found the squat and sullen fortress of the giant.

Diarmuid had come in search of three sisters, abducted by the giant almost a year before. Perhaps because of his bold-ness—or because he offered himself meek-ly as a servant to the giant—Diarmuid was admitted to the fortress. He found the gi-ant in his hall with his prisoners; but only one of them, apparently strong enough to resist the giant's spells, was still a woman. The others had been transformed—one into a dainty hound called a whippet, the other into a piebald filly.

The giant observed Diarmuid's surprise with amusement, and he hired the young man as his servant. The master of the wood feared no one, least of all a mere mortal. The only weapon that could kill him was a giant-forged sword that was hidden—like the soul of the troll of Lapland—in an al-most impenetrable prison, the innermost of three concentric chambers at the heart of the fortress; the chamber doors were locked with keys that never left the giant's

possession. And if the giant could not be slain, neither could his spells be undone, since the source of his magic lay in a wand of beech that he kept always on his body.

Other warriors had tried to defeat him and all had failed. But Diar-muid was an especially resourceful foe—both a well-trained fighter, as swift and silent as a cat, and a peculiarly dextrous man, as light-fingered as any thief. He bided his time for some days and did the giant's bidding without complaint. When the giant slept, he conferred with the wom-an prisoner, while her sisters, trapped in animal form, watched him with sad, hope-ful eyes. From the lady, Diarmuid learned the secret of the sword and beech wand.

One night, when all the castle lay asleep and the only sound to be heard was the whispering of leaves outside the windows, he walked alone through the corridors of the fortress to its cold heart, which was sealed by an iron door. Outside the door, on a pallet long enough for two human men, the giant lay—watchman to the secret of his life. He was asleep. From a chain around the massive neck, Diarmuid slipped the keys to the chambers behind the door, and so slow and gentle were his fingers that the giant never stirred.

He shifted on his pallet and grunted, however, when Diarmuid unlocked the first door. The very iron spoke aloud: "Master!" it said mournfully, and its sighs drifted through the corridors of the castle. The giant shifted again when the door within the outer chamber opened, for that door cried out to him, too. And by the

Some giants, great in magic and grasping in nature, acquired human slaves. The
Irish giant of the Brown Beech Wood kept three women captive; one he left in her
own shape, but for amusement he changed her sisters into a lap dog and a little horse.

Even against the giants' ancient power, human bravery
prevailed. The Beech Wood giant died because a man found
his castle's heart and took the sword concealed there.

Strange were the routes to the giants' worlds. In Scotland once, a jewel-like seed thrown to the ground grew into a vine ladder that twisted to the heavens. The lad who climbed its leafy rungs found at the top a kingdom in the clouds.

time Diarmuid had opened the door to the innermost chamber, the giant of the Brown Beech Wood was on his feet.

He was too late. Deep within the central chamber, on the foundation stone of the castle, the warrior Diarmuid stood. Above his head was raised a luminous sword, as long as Diarmuid was tall. With a savage scream, the giant lurched forward. Diarmuid gave his battle cry in turn, then leaped and plunged the sword into the giant's heart, so that the blood of the old one ran down the blade.

And there the guardian of the Brown Beech Wood died. Diarmuid took his wand of enchantment and returned the women to their rightful forms. Then the four mortals left the wood. Behind them, the fortress crumbled to the ground, making a cairn of giant stones for its vanquished ruler. And as the humans rode away, the great beech trees blackened, withered and faded into invisibility.

n ot all challenges to giants had revenge or rescue for their primary motive. Some mortals invaded giants' territories in search of treasure. Hidden among the rulers of this ancient race were the objects of a wonder-filled past — an era lost forever, it seemed to humankind, whose world grew more and more prosaic as the centuries rolled away. In the realms of the giants were magic wands and swords, such as those of the Beech Wood, as well as caldrons that gave forth endless meat and drink or restored the dead to the semblance of life. The giants were also said to possess gold that exceeded the hoards of the richest human kings. Inevitably, these temptations were enough to persuade some adventurers to dare the power and the anger of the old ones. The humans came not as warriors but as thieves, and some were humble folk indeed.

Among these trespassers, none was so famous as a Scottish wastrel known to history only as Jock. He lived with his mother in a fishing village by the Firth of Lorne on the west coast of the country. But Jock was no fisherman, and although there were both farms and pastures near his home, he neither farmed nor herded sheep. He spent his days in idleness, loafing and boasting of the great things meant for him in life.

Jock's mother kept him as well as she could. He was her only son, and she had no husband living; Jock eased the loneliness. But she could not keep him very well, for she subsisted on the yield of a tiny garden plot and a single cow.

One cold year, the garden's produce was too meager to support the two of them. The woman sent Jock out to sell the animal. It was man's work, and just the kind that the young man liked, because it would give him a chance to show his shrewdness. He set off toward the nearest market town, leading the cow.

He never reached the place. At a bend in the road, he met a woman. She was old, but her hair still showed the gold and her eyes the blue of the Vikings who had long ago flooded Scotland with their kind. She hailed Jock and asked him his business, and when he told her, she set about a painstaking examination of the cow.

"It is a bonny cow," she said at last, "and I can give you something worth far more than money for her." She fixed him with a glittering eye and from her cloak drew a small bundle wrapped in silk. In it was a wonder—a cluster of small seeds shaped like beans but as iridescent as jewels.

As Jock stared, the woman mumbled over the little gems, turning them in her fingers. "Dropped from the world tree," she said. "Guides to treasure."

Whether Jock believed these words or not—whether, indeed, he had any notion of northern tales of a world tree—no one ever knew. But clearly the little gems were unusual. He took them and gave the woman the cow. With a sidelong glance, she hobbled off. Jock made for home with the pretty baubles in his

pocket. They did not look so lovely when he showed them to his mother. Their luster had gone. In his palm lay nothing more than dull beans. With a cry for the loss of the cow, the woman thrust his hand away. The beans fell onto the ground beside her cottage door. Then she fled, weeping, into the house, leaving Jock to salvage his treasure. But the beans had disappeared—

swallowed, it seemed, by the earth itself.

With a shrug, Jock left the cottage for the alehouse. He had no work to do, and his mother's weeping irritated him. He remained away until dusk, when he staggered home to his pallet by the hearth. He fell asleep immediately.

In the small hours, he was awakened by a rustling near the door, a sound as soft as the night-sighs of the sea. Listening, he thought he also heard faint chimes or perhaps distant harp notes. He rose to investigate. Outside the door, swaying to almost soundless music, a mighty vine reached upward. Tendril after tendril searched in the air; leaf after leaf uncurled, higher and higher, until leaves and tendrils made silhouettes against the paling sky and wound themselves among the setting stars. It was a ladder to the heavens that grew from the ground. Enthralled, the young man began to climb it at the first light of dawn, ascending the viny column steadily until his muscles screamed and sweat stung his eyes. From time to time, he glanced down and saw his village growing smaller, saw the patchwork fields spread out to the east and the misty morning sea to the west. Above his head, the vine reached into cloud. Before long he gained this ceiling and passed through its gray wetness, emerging into bright sunlight. Above his head was a vault of purest blue. All about the vine spread a rolling field of cloud. Across it, far away, stood a castle. Clinging to the vine, Jock cautiously put a foot to the cloud. It was as springy and solid as turf. He tested it, then let go of the vine and set out for the castle to see what he might find there.

Guarding the gate was a woman. She seemed as tall as his mother had when he was a very small child: His head reached barely to her knee. The vast hand dangling by her skirt was ornamented with rings that winked gold, red and blue in the sunlight, and around her neck was a twisted band of immense pearls. The fear Jock had felt at first now vanished, replaced by greed. Here was opportunity for a man with his wits about him. He tugged at the giantess's skirt, and when she bent her head to him, he gave her his most charming and ingenuous smile.

But her gaze was challenging. "Earthling," she said, "how came you here?"

Jock gestured to the green tips of the vine piercing the clouds in the distance. Her face grew somber. She said, "If you are found here, you die, for the old ones know that your kind are bane to them."

"Will you not shelter me, lady?" said Jock softly. And the giantess, with a maternal gesture as old as time, gathered him in her arms and took him into the fortress. Through lofty corridors they went, then down a winding stair into a cavernous hall. A hearth fire – a veritable conflagration by mortal standards – blazed there. The giantess placed Jock in a basket near this fire, among a nest of apples as large as humans' butter churns. She covered him with a cloth as tenderly as if he had been a child.

"Hide here, earthling," she said, "and make no move until dusk. Then return to your own world." She left him.

Jock did as he was told, although he peeked from his fragrant lair from time to time to scout the terrain. In this way, he saw the lord of the place enter the hall, demanding meat. This giant was as shaggy as a beast; he flung himself down at a table that stood in the hall and pounded on its boards with his fists. The giantess served him his food and drink in silence, and he fell upon the fare, gnawing and grunting, his black eyes wandering around the room. Under the table at his feet rested a hen as large as a lamb. While Jock watched, the bird gave a triumphant cackle. The giant nudged it aside with his foot and picked up the egg the hen had laid. The egg was solid gold.

For an hour or more, the giant ate and drank while Jock huddled in the apple basket, sometimes watching and sometimes dozing. At last, the castle's master fell forward onto the littered table, spilling wine and scattering slabs of bread. He began to snore in deafening measures.

Jock seized his chance. He crawled from the basket and hurried across the floor to the hen. Clapping a hand across her eyes and beak, he lifted the bird and made for freedom. Outside, he raced across the clouds – now stained rose and lavender by the setting sun – and swiftly descended the vine. As he slithered down its trunk, the hen shrank in his grasp, so that when he appeared before his mother, he carried a fowl the size of any other. She regarded him without comprehension as he displayed his prize and told his tale. But when the hen produced an egg of gold, her

Alerted by the cries of his stolen harp, the cloud giant pursued the human who had robbed him. But the thief cut the vine, and the giant plummeted to his death.

expression turned to a mixture of fear and avarice. She took the bird with trembling hands and clasped it to her bosom. Afraid to let it out of her sight, she made a little enclosure and kept the hen beside the hearth.

A curious element in the accounts of Jock's adventure was that none of them make mention of his neighbors' reaction to his activities: The villagers apparently were unaware of the magic in their midst. It seemed that he and his mother stepped outside human space and time when the vine sprouted beside their cottage and rose to the clouds. In any case, the situation gave Jock, who grew hourly more ambitious, great opportunity. The next day, he climbed the vine and again returned with treasure—gold amulets shaped like the hammer of the old god Thor and inlaid with garnets. His mother buried these beneath the dirt floor of the cottage.

Jock's third ascent, however, brought disaster. His mother, standing at the base of the vine, saw and heard it all. High above, Jock emerged from the ceiling of cloud and began his descent. In one arm he clutched a golden harp. Suddenly, the instrument's strings gave a cry of agony. A roar in heaven answered it, and the cloud ceiling shifted and sagged under blasts of thunder high above. Jock let the wailing harp fall to earth and slid down the vine after it. As he touched the ground, a pair of boots appeared at the top of the vine. The trunk swayed to and fro in the sky. His hands trembling and bloodied, Jock swung around to his mother and screamed once, a shout of pure and deathly fear.

But terror quickened the woman's wits: She thrust an ax into Jock's grasp. And Jock acted. He hacked at the swaying vine while, high above his head, the giant clung and bellowed. Through leaf and tendril and trunk Jock slashed. The vine shuddered as if in pain. At last, with a terrible groan, it leaned slowly westward, gathered speed and fell toward the sea. As the mighty shaft of greenness toppled, the giant at its crown released his hold. Roaring his death song, he plunged through the air into the waters below.

The sky itself seemed to lament: Tears of rain fell for hours, until at last the heavy clouds parted and drifted away. Nothing was left then of the giant's kingdom but shreds of mist and floating scraps of white. The thief had triumphed.

Accounts of Jock's life after that differ in most particulars, but all agree that he and his mother lived handsomely on the giant's gold. And Jock was but one of many. As the years passed, mortals pursued giants more and more. The old ones' time was ending; the day would come when even the most ferocious of them would die by human hands.

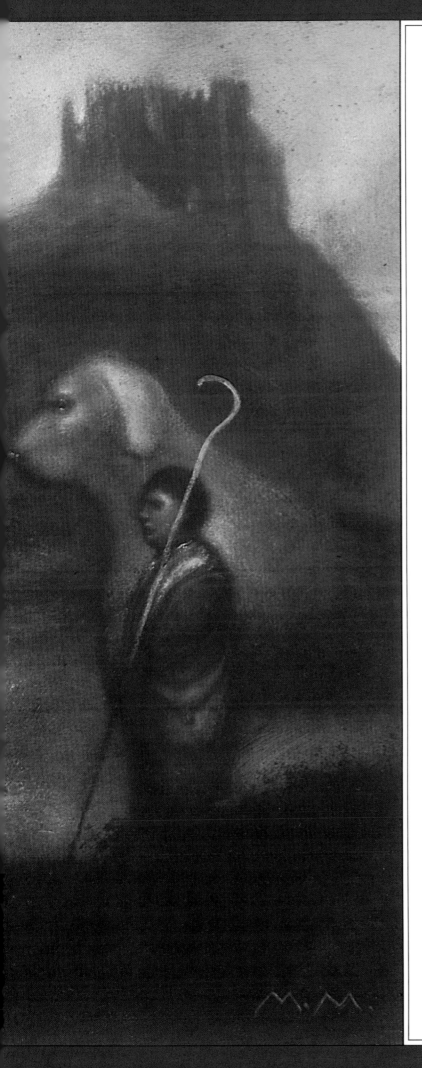

Kilhwch and Olwen

Survivors of the world's first age, giants were cloaked in ancient mystery, and tales of how men conquered them often were clouded with hints of venerable ritual. Such was the case in Britain when Arthur was King. He pitted his warriors against Ysbaddaden Penkawr—meaning in Welsh, "Hawthorn, King of Giants." At stake was the hand of Ysbaddaden's daughter, who was human in form and more than human in beauty.

The tale began with a knight named Kilhwch, Arthur's cousin. Kilhwch had a curse set on him by his stepmother: to marry Ysbaddaden's daughter or spend his life without a woman. Winning the maid was a formidable task, for Ysbaddaden's life depended on her. The giant's fate was to die on the day she left him for a mortal man, and he was vigilant in guarding her. More than one man had perished in pursuit of the young woman.

Knowing this, Kilhwch rode to Arthur's court, where he invoked the names of all of Arthur's company and his kinship to the King and asked for aid to win the maiden. Arthur granted the boon.

So one fine summer day, a brave company arrived at the giant's castle. Kilhwch was astride his gold-bridled horse and with him were the noblest of Arthur's knights—led by Kay and Bedevere, whose swords always found their marks and left wounds no physician could heal.

The castle stood on a wide green plain alive with sheep; the gatekeeper was a mortal shepherd, but his dog was a mastiff the size of a horse. Although the man was a morose creature, it was he who showed Kilhwch the giant's daughter. She was as lovely as the day. Her hair, the poets later sang, was yellower than broom, her skin whiter than sea foam, her glance brighter than that of the bravest falcon. Where she walked, it was said, white trefoils grew, and so she was named Olwen, meaning "she of the white track."

Kilhwch was entranced. He spoke to her; she answered him sweetly and told him what he must do to win her.

With his company, therefore, Kilhwch followed Olwen into her father's fortress. They killed the guards who barred their entry. This did not seem to distress the maiden. With a smile and the briefest gesture, she showed the way to Ysbaddaden's hall. Then she turned into a corridor and vanished from their sight.

The men strode into the giant's echoing hall and found him waiting, looming dark in an archway. Ysbaddaden returned their greeting and heard them out when they asked for Olwen's hand, but all he said was that they should come back the next day for an answer. As they turned to go, however, he stooped into the shadows. When he rose to face them again, a spear flew from his hand directly at the mortals. Swifter than sight, Bedevere leaped and caught the weapon; without a word, he flung it, and it pierced the giant's knee. The great creature cursed them for the pain, but he let them leave unharmed.

The savage act was repeated the next day and again the next, when Kilhwch caught the spear and flung it through the giant's eye. At last Ysbaddaden's prelude was over, and he agreed to parley.

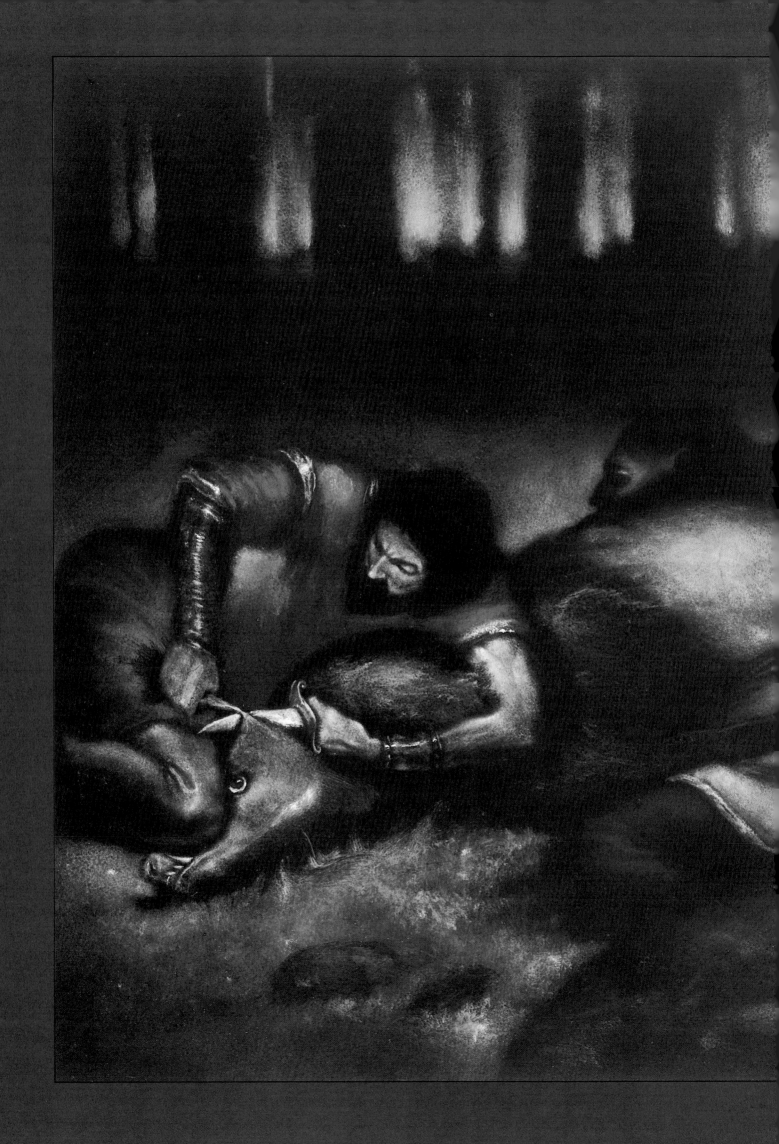

As Olwen had said he would, Ysbaddaden agreed that Kilhwch should have her—if he paid the proper bride price.

"Name what you want and I will pay it," said Kilhwch.

Ysbaddaden sat down. He chanted his demands, which were many. He asked the mortals to provide a bride feast on a giant's scale, to plow and sow and reap enchanted fields for grain and for flax to make a wedding veil, to steal a certain fabulous hamper that provided endless food and a harp that played by itself, to catch the magic birds of Rhiannon, the Fairy Queen, whose songs drove away all care. Thirty-nine tasks Ysbaddaden named, and as he recited each, Kilhwch calmly replied, "I can get that easily, although you think that I cannot." And at the end, Kilhwch repeated, "All of these things I will easily get, for mortal men will help me. I shall have Olwen and you will lose your life." Then, with the company of knights, he left the hall.

The poets did not say how the tasks were accomplished, only that they were, because all of Arthur's warriors fanned out across Britain to help Kilhwch defeat the Giant King. Of one task the poets did sing—that of taking from the boar Twrch Trwyth a comb of bristle and shears of tusk to trim the giant's hair.

A mighty chase it was, for the boar was a man under an enchantment, and it had man's skill and cunning. It could be hunted only with certain hounds and these hounds could be handled only by a man who was himself hidden in an enchanted prison. The hounds were found. The man was found, it was said, through the instructions of the most ancient of animals, which were named as the Ousel of Kilgwri, the Stag of Rhedenvre, the Owl of Cwm Cawlwyd, the Eagle of Gwernabwy and the Salmon of Llyn Llyw.

Still, the chase was hard, and Arthur

lost good men to the tusks of the boar. They followed it to Ireland and fought it there. It swam the seas to Wales, and they pursued it; they had it at bay once in the Severn River, and there they wrested the shears of tusk from it. It escaped them once more and they followed it to Cornwall, where they seized the bristle comb. But the boar they did not seize. It fled into the sea and was never seen again.

Thus after many months of travail, the last battle was ended and the last task complete. The treasures were taken to the giant and spread before him in his hall. Ysbaddaden surveyed them impassively. Then he sent for his daughter. Olwen appeared, robed in scarlet and adorned with a neck torque of twisted gold. At her father's command, she stood at Kilhwch's side, thus passing from the power of the old world into the protection of the new.

The end of the strange rite began: Ysbaddaden demanded to be shaved and combed with the tusk and bristle of Twrch Trwyth. This was done. Then Kilhwch said, "Are you now clean?"

"I am," replied the giant.

"And is Olwen mine?"

"She is," said Ysbaddaden, and added bitterly, "Not by my will but because of the strength of many mortals against me."

Kilhwch made no reply. He waited, and at last the giant said, "It is time for you to kill me."

Kilhwch nodded gravely and gestured, and a servant came to him. The man took the giant into his own castle courtyard and, with a single blow of his ax, beheaded Ysbaddaden. Then Kilhwch gave his hand to Ysbaddaden's beautiful daughter, whom he kept by his side for the rest of his life. He took the fortress and the land for himself. All that was left of the ancient Giant King was a massive, tattered head on a stake, staring sightlessly out at the green plain.

Chapter Four

The Twilight of Power

Before it was tamed by successive waves of seafaring peoples, Sicily was a place that conjured dread in the human heart. In the waters around the island swirled vicious whirlpools formed by the conflicting currents of the Ionian and Tyrrhenian Seas. On the offshore islets were volcanoes said to shelter the gods of fire and of the winds. Sicily itself was rimmed by rocky headlands and broken by smoking volcanoes, but any adventurer who went there had to face a danger worse than these: The island was roamed by giants called Cyclopes – Greek for "ring-eyed," in reference to the fact that each had a single, central eye.

The Cyclopes were slow-witted barbarians who lived in caves, but they had not always been so backward. The Greeks said that the race was created before humankind and that the first Cyclopes had been master craftsmen – smiths who forged such treasures as the silver bow of Artemis, goddess of the hunt. As the centuries rolled by, however, the Cyclopes degenerated and lost all knowledge of their art. No one knew why this was so. Indeed, little

could be told of the Cyclopes' past except that they had long ago left their first home, the northern mountains of Thrace, and wandered westward and south, finally settling in Sicily. The ragtag remnants of the race subsisted there as shepherds, the chroniclers said, "without laws, ships, markets or knowledge of agriculture."

Humans, meanwhile, were growing in power and boldness, ranging ever farther across the world. Inevitably, some of them dared the waters of the Cyclopes' refuge.

Of these adventurers, the most famous was Odysseus of Ithaca, a wily fighter who took part in the long and ultimately successful siege of Troy. After the sack of that city, he struck off across the Aegean and the Mediterranean with a shipful of Greek warriors. A few weeks of sailing brought him to the roiling waters of Sicily. Negotiating their perils without mishap, Odysseus beached the ship and led a small party of men inland to explore. This country seemed promising at first. The interior of the island was thick-ly wood-

NEARY

ed and had rich volcanic soil; there was even an abundance of natural shelter: Caves half hidden by hanging laurel pockmarked the mountainous terrain.

Odysseus and his men entered one of these caves. As soon as their eyes grew accustomed to the dimness, the Greeks saw that they had invaded someone's home. Nets heavy with draining cheeses hung from the stony walls, and at the back of the cave was a pen for a flock of kids.

With a rogue's grin and a jerk of his thumb, Odysseus set his men to work building a fire at the center of the cavern. They slaughtered two of the kids and roasted them, and they helped themselves to cheese. It was a rough and merry feast. The wineskins passed freely, and as the light outside began to fade and the fire died down, the men drowsed. They were therefore unprepared for the arrival of the cave's owner.

A flock of sheep as large as ponies preceded him, crowding the cavern mouth and bleating to be milked. At the rear of the flock, flanked by goats, was a Cyclops. He was formidable, more than twice the size of even the largest human, and Odysseus and his warriors felt the chill of fear. But the giant's single eye did not turn to the depths of the cavern where the men had feasted. Mumbling and grunting to himself, the creature heaved a boulder into the mouth of the cave, thus sealing himself – and the Greeks, who could not possibly have moved such a stone – firmly within. Then he squatted on his massive haunches and milked his ewes.

Only when the animals had been penned and the wooden milk buckets set against the cavern wall did the Cyclops wander into the interior of his dwelling. At the heap of smoldering coals that was the last of the Greeks' fire, he halted. The single eye stared dully down at the remains of the feast. In a puzzled way, the giant examined the men who sat motionless beside the coals. He appeared to consider the situation for some moments. At last he said to Odysseus, who had risen, "You killed my animals and ate them."

"Gentle monster," replied Odysseus smoothly, "remember the duties of hospitality to travelers."

The Cyclops, however, was not prepared to parley. One huge arm shot out and encircled two of Odysseus' men. He wheeled and threw the pair headfirst against the cavern wall so that their skulls shattered. Then, without even a glance at the remaining Greeks, the Cyclops fed, carefully peeling the still-warm flesh from the dead men's bones, patiently chewing at muscle and sinew and lapping loudly at the pooling blood.

The Greeks, heeding a signal from their leader, kept still throughout the terrible meal. There was nothing they could do: All of them together were not nearly a match for the giant. When the Cyclops finished eating, he kicked the bones aside and fell into noisy slumber. But his prisoners remained where they were, for the giant remained alert, opening his eye at the slightest move among them. Besides, as Odysseus remarked in a whisper, if they killed him while he slept, they would remain prisoners forever. Only giant hands could shift the stone that blocked the entrance to the cave.

The monster was no match for crafty Odysseus, however. In the morning, the Cyclops herded his flocks out into the sunlight, rolling the stone again into place at the cave mouth. The Greeks, at the instruction of their commander, removed a pole of olivewood from the goat pen, sharpened it with their hunting knives and tempered the tip in a fire. Then they hid the spear beneath a pile of dung and settled down to wait.

The Cyclops returned in the evening and milked his animals. Then, with the same matter-of-fact efficiency he had shown the evening before, he killed two more of Odysseus' men and ate them. When the Cyclops was sated, Odysseus approached him with a wineskin.

"An offering, lord," said the Greek. "This is the nectar of the gods."

The Cyclops eyed the man suspiciously, but he took the wineskin and drank. Blinking his single eye, he drank again, this time more deeply.

It was fine wine that Odysseus had given him, and it was not diluted with water, as was the custom in Greece. The Cyclops, having tasted nothing in his life stronger than milk, was stupefied by it. He collapsed, breathing stertorously.

Then Odysseus acted. He withdrew the sharpened olivewood pole from its hiding place, stood over the unconscious giant and plunged the tip into the huge eye, bearing down while his men spun the shaft, as shipbuilders spun the drills when boring timbers. Blood sizzled from the eye; humors coiled and hissed around the pole. The Cyclops surged screaming to his feet, and Odysseus and his men leaped out of range.

They spent the rest of that night dodging the blinded creature as he groped around his cave, lurching after every rustle of movement, sobbing with pain and spitting curses at the Greeks. He was an easy enemy, however, and not a man was lost.

Finally, the Cyclops fell silent. He sank to his knees and began to fumble along the cavern wall, feeling his way toward the entrance. When he found it, he pushed the imprisoning stone away. The morning light showed gray in the cave mouth.

But the Cyclops was not finished with them. His dull brain, it seemed, had formed a plan for revenge. Where the stone had been, he himself crouched. His great hands dangled between his knees, flexing and unflexing while he waited for the humans to try to pass.

Odysseus was rarely at a loss, and his wits did not fail him now. He gestured, and his men freed the giant's sheep. Odysseus gave one animal a push, directing it toward the entrance to the cavern. When it butted up against the Cyclops' knee, the hands rose to it; the mighty fingers fumbled at the head and the fleece of the back.

"Good beast," the Cyclops muttered, and with a tap of surprising gentleness, he sent the sheep on its way into the open air.

Now Odysseus knew what to do. Using vinelike twigs drawn from the animal pen, he strapped each of his men under the belly of a sheep. One by one, he urged the

animals toward the cave mouth. Over each sheep the giant brooded, feeling along the back and flanks to make sure the animal had no rider. But he did not feel the bellies of the beasts, and never sensed the passengers who clung there. Every man escaped.

When they were free, Odysseus gave a crow of triumph. "If anyone asks who blinded you, old one, tell them it was Odysseus of Ithaca," he shouted. Then he and his men drove the Cyclops' flock through the mountains to the shore where the ship lay; the sheep would provide them meat as they sailed on to other adventures. Behind the Greeks, the giant pawed helplessly at his bloodied face. He wept and railed and cursed, and his voice echoed over the hills. He lurched across his island, following the sound of the retreating voices, and when he reached the rocks of the shore, he hurled boulders blindly into the sea after the enemy. But Odysseus gave no more thought to the primitive creature he had maimed, except to boast of his cunning in defeating it.

It was often thus in the final age of giants. Where once they had ruled the earth, they now were outcasts, driven into obscure corners of the world by the waxing strength of humankind. At the same time, age weakened them. That process was far slower than the way aging affected mortals, but it was inexorable. The latter-day giants were but pale husks of their ancestors, and humans were quite willing to take them on in combat.

In the course of ten years of adventuring in the Mediterranean, Odysseus and his fellow Greeks invaded the island retreat of the Cyclopes, one-eyed giants. When a giant trapped them in his cave, they put out his eye with a stake.

It became, in fact, a point of honor among the citizens of Europe to claim that their cities were founded on the bones of giants slain by humans. The Flemish, for instance, said that a giant named Antigonus once inhabited a castle on the River Scheldt. From this fortress (whose ruins were still to be seen in the Middle Ages) he terrorized all travelers, demanding exorbitant tolls for the privilege of passage through his territory—and cutting off the hand of anyone who refused to pay. Finally, a prince of the province overthrew and killed him.

Around the site of Antigonus' castle then grew the rich merchant port of Antwerp, a name its citizens said derived from the Flemish phrase *hantworp*, meaning "hand tossing," a reference to Antigonus' brutal practice. In truth, the name of the port probably comes from *an t'Werf*—or "the city on the wharf"—but this did not deter the residents from asserting a more impressive derivation. Their city arms have always shown a three-towered silver castle surmounted by two red hands—the hands of his victims.

More grandiose even than the Flemish tale was the claim made by that imaginative British chronicler, Geoffrey of Monmouth. Eager to link his island to the glories of the ancient world, Geoffrey wrote that Britain—or Albion, as it was then called—was inhabited by a race of giants until the invasion of a mighty warrior called Brut, a Prince descended from the hero Aeneas of Troy. Brut's armies routed the giants and killed all of them except one, called Gogmagog. For amusement, the Prince then decided to pit this creature in single combat against his own ally, a man named Corineus. The fight was held on a plain in what is now Devonshire, on the southwest coast. The giant, who stood twelve cubits (about twenty feet) tall, immediately took the offensive, seizing his rival in a crushing embrace. In his rage and pain, Corineus was charged with superhuman strength. He lifted Gogmagog and flung him from a promontory into the sea, where, wrote Geoffrey, "falling on the sides of the rocks, he was torn to pieces and colored the waves with his blood." The rock from which the giant fell was at a place called Haw, near Plymouth, and was ever after known as Lam Goëmagot, or "Gogmagog's Leap." Then, according to Geoffrey, the island, cleared of giants and open to human settlement, was named Britain in honor of its conqueror, Brut.

Geoffrey was a mythmaker speculating on an age completely obscured by the mists of time. There was little evidence to support his version of events and much to undermine it. What, for example, accounted for the presence of giants in Britain long after Brut was alleged to have destroyed the race? During the era of chivalry, knights fought them regularly. Indeed, in Britain as elsewhere in Europe, the killing of giants became a test of courage and knightly merit.

*C*hivalry, with its pageantry and ritual, was but a thin veneer on what was still a savage age. The knights of the old tales might be enjoined to loyalty toward their monarchs, to generosity, justice and gentleness toward their fellows, to

AB 1896

protection of the weak. They might be the most accomplished of poets, the most elegant of courtiers, the most courteous of lovers, and there were rules to govern all of these activities. But the very essence of their being was war. They were trained as fighters almost from infancy, and they spent the greater part of their lives in mounted battle. Fighting defined them.

This ethic was celebrated in many a song about the warriors who served the Frankish Emperor Charlemagne. The most valiant of these knights were called peers, because their powers were almost equal, or paladins, because they were inmates of the imperial palace. The most renowned of them was Roland, nephew of the Emperor. A fight with a giant brought Roland his nimbus of glory.

The giant lived on an island south of

Howling with pain and rage, the blinded Cyclops followed his tormentors to Sicily's rocky shore. He hurled boulders after their vessel, but the adventurers escaped with ease.

Spain, then held by the Saracens, enemies of the Franks. His name was Ferragus and his reputation was terrifying. He was said to dwell in a fortress of gleaming metal. His possessions included a sculptured head of brass that could answer any question put to it and a magic horse of wood that could fly through the air.

Ferragus issued a challenge to Charlemagne after the Franks invaded Spain, thereby encroaching on the giant's territory. He offered to meet any of the Emperor's knights in single combat.

Whatever inward qualms they may have felt, the paladins vied to represent their ruler and give Ferragus his due. All of the Frankish company gathered on a plain not far from the giant's fortress. Then Ogier the Dane, Rinaldo of the White Thorn, Constantine of Rome, Howel of Nantes—

great fighters all – rode one by one into the field against Ferragus. All fell before him. He simply leaned from his high saddle as they approached and swept each man from his horse and bore him off to imprisonment in the gleaming castle.

Seeing how helpless his warriors were against such strength, the Emperor ordered a truce, but he had not reckoned on the rage of Roland, who demanded the chance to redeem the honor of court and country. Charlemagne had no choice but to let the young knight go.

The battle Roland fought with Ferragus was a curious mixture of savage violence and the most delicate courtesy. As he had the others, Ferragus swept the Frankish knight from horseback at once, set him across his saddle as if he were a child, and carried him back toward his fortress. Roland, however, contrived to knock the giant from the saddle to the ground. He struck at Ferragus with his sword then, but the giant's skin was as resistant to the thrust as the finest steel known.

They battled through an afternoon, first with swords, then with fists, stones and clubs. When daylight began to fade, the giant called a truce. He lay down on the field to sleep, and so perfect was Roland's courtesy that Ferragus slept unmolested: The laws of chivalry would not permit an attack on an opponent under such circumstances. In fact, Roland, seeing that the giant slept without a pillow, placed a stone on the ground under the great head to give Ferragus ease.

This inspired in the giant a certain trust of the man. Apparently the two conversed during the truce, and Ferragus revealed that he had only one vulnerable spot on his body – his navel. That, of course, was the giant's undoing, for when the courtesies of the truce were ended, Roland leaped ferociously upon the enemy and thrust his sword into Ferragus' navel, dealing him a fatal wound. After that, Charlemagne and his troops stormed the giant's fortress and released their companions.

No doubt they embellished the tale to better reflect chivalric ideals. But if their portrayal of Ferragus had any truth at all, then he was a rare representative of his declining race – a throwback to a time of grandeur and high-mindedness.

Stories concerning King Arthur's knights of the Round Table paint a very different picture. The giants these warriors chanced upon were degenerate horrors. They were clothed in skins and armed with clubs. They took pleasure in giving pain. Some of them were man-eaters.

An especially vivid glimpse of giants in their decay is provided by a tale about a knight named Erec. He was a Breton Prince, the son of Lac, and a favored and dashing member of Arthur's company. In his youth he won for a wife a maiden named Enide, and such was her beauty and kindness that he forgot, for a time, the most basic tenet of chivalry.

He took Enide to his father's lands in Brittany, where he secluded himself with her for many months and gave himself up to pleasure. Erec became the most uxorious of husbands. No longer did he present himself at tournaments to prove his skill. No longer did he go into the world in search of adventure. He remained untested in the very things that mattered most. Whispers, and then laughter, began far away at King Arthur's court. The knight who absented himself from battle was no knight at all.

Word of the scorn of Erec's peers spread throughout Britain, carried by bards and minstrels and wandering knights. It crept into the halls of King Lac's fortress, whispered by squires and servants. At last, it reached the ears of Enide.

She was grief-stricken to an extent that is difficult to understand now. In those days, the knight who failed to seek adventure declared himself a coward, and death was preferable to such dishonor. A wife's honor was inextricably linked with her lord's. Enide, who was inclined to self-blame, wept at the knowledge that she had seduced her husband into shame. Yet she did not tell Erec what she knew. She feared his anger.

Soon enough, he learned the truth, however. In the airy chamber where they slept, Erec heard her whispering drowsily to herself of how even the laundresses laughed at him. He sat up among the tumbled bedclothes and shook his wife awake. He ordered her to speak.

As he listened to what she had to tell him, his face grew pale and set. But all he said was that he would ride out on the open road, and that Enide would make the journey with him as witness to his deeds. This was a cruelty, for such journeys were hard and full of danger, but Erec was a very young man, and being shamed in his wife's eyes had caused him to hate her.

They made a fine pair as they cantered away from Lac's fortress, an image of chivalry just before its flower faded. In fluttering silks and nets of silver, riding a dappled palfrey, Enide followed a path through the checkered fields that lay around the fortress. Behind her came Erec on a smoky gray. His helmet was fluted with gold, his hauberk was of silver mesh, and his greaves were polished steel. Through the shimmering rye and barley fields they went, by green pastures fenced with hedgerows, out of the settled lands and into the forest that brooded beyond.

The tale of their journey has the shifting, dreamlike quality common to most accounts of questing knights. They traveled in no particular direction and spoke little. They were set upon by brigands and attacked by outlaw knights who hid in those uncharted woods. These Erec defeated, for he was brilliantly skilled with lance and broadsword, and he was a man without fear. Then they came upon giants.

The adventure began in a haunted stretch of forest whose location was never recorded. Amid the gloom and silence of the wood, a young woman wandered, weeping. Erec halted her and heard her tale; then he left her with Enide and rode in the direction she had given him.

He came soon to a clearing, and there he saw the woman's companion, a fair-haired man astride a horse. The man was naked. His hands were bound behind his back with thongs, and his ankles were secured by a strap that passed beneath the horse's belly. Down his bare and straining

In chivalry's golden days, victory over the waning race of giants was proof of valor.

So it was with furious delight that the knight Roland challenged the colossus Ferragus.

thighs ran a network of bloody rivulets. His bent back had been purpled by blows and was deeply lacerated in places.

Beside his captors, this man appeared no larger than a child, his horse no bigger than a dog. He was held by a pair of giants, swarthy and twisted, clothed in skins and armed with spiked clubs. Even as Erec approached, they continued to torment the human who had ridden into their territory. The giants mumbled and laughed as their victim screamed at the impact of the spiked clubs. Sweat beaded on their dark faces, and spittle whitened the corners of their mouths.

When Erec shouted a challenge, one of the giants grunted with amusement. "Another man," he said, and he gave an anticipatory twirl to his club.

Those were the giant's last words. Raising his lance, Erec charged. The giant crouched to meet the onslaught, but the knight's well-aimed lance tip found its mark in the huge skull. As the giant toppled, Erec released the embedded weapon. The other giant was upon him now, swinging his club down toward Erec's head. But the knight held his shield high to break the blow. From beneath the shield, his great broadsword flashed. The point buried itself deep in the giant's chest.

With a deafening wail, the giant fell. Erec wheeled his horse out of the way. Then he dismounted, hacked the great bodies into pieces, and strewed the guts across the grass. Finally, he turned to the giants' prisoner.

The man was a knight called Cadoc of Tabriol. He had been riding with his lady when the giants seized him and made him their toy. Now, following the custom in such cases of rescue, he offered himself as Erec's liege man. Erec declined. Instead, he sent Cadoc to his lady for healing and told him that, when he was well again, he should ride to Arthur's court. "Present yourself as a gift to the King from me," said Erec. In the stilted language of chivalry, he added, "Be careful not to conceal from him with what peril I set free both your life and body."

This Cadoc faithfully did—and soon others followed suit. As the months passed, a succession of knights appeared at Arthur's court, arriving from various parts of Britain to offer their loyalty to the King in Erec's name and to recount stories of Erec's valor. These messengers spoke, too, of Enide's steadfast tenderness and of the new-blossoming love between husband and wife. When Erec at last returned to the world of men, he returned with both honor and marital happiness restored.

Erec's encounter with the monsters in the meadow had a certain symmetry to it. This was, after all, a test of fighter against fighter. The giants' advantage in strength was offset by the knight's advantages of skill and—as the troubadours would have it—virtue. But the reality of the last days of giants was rarely so tidy. Behind their descent into brutishness lay the tragedy of declining powers of mind. Once the possessors of all knowledge, they had become witless, muddled, almost bestial. At the dawn of the world, the very gods had envied the giants their wisdom. Now the

Without hesitation, without fear, King Arthur's knight Erec set himself against two
brutal giants who threatened him. One died on Erec's spear, the other on his sword.

humblest mortals held them in contempt.

A French story sums up this pitiable turnabout. It tells of a miller who lived along the banks of the Loire. The miller was a simple man, content that his mill sails should turn, that his wife's hens should lay, that his cow should give milk and his garden yield turnips and cabbages. The miller lived in lean times, but he was thrifty and jealous of his purse in the way of peasants everywhere.

One day, a wandering giant, accompanied by a female of his kind, drove a herd of cows into the rocky hills above the mill and settled there. This giant was no colossus. He was only a few feet taller than a man, but he was immensely strong in the manner of all those with giants' blood. Under a matted thatch of hair, his face was wart-covered and twisted. The miller, repulsed by his features and all too aware of the power in his heavy muscles, gave him the contemptuous name of Ogre. And his thoughts grew bitter indeed when Ogre began to appear at the mill and demand grain or flour.

For some months, the miller paid the tithe. But his careful nature could not bear the waste. A day came when, seeing Ogre making his slow way down the hillside, the miller hid with his wife under the straw of the cow's byre.

There was no sound but the muffled clucking and scratching of the hens outside and the rustling of the cow as it shifted in its stall. Then Ogre's rasping voice called out, first near the cottage door, then at the mill. At last, the giant ducked into the darkness of the byre, sniffing the air and mumbling the miller's name.

The miller and his wife did not stir. Ogre crouched in the small shelter, snuffling, muttering. At length, with a grunt of frustration, he punched the cow in the head and left. The cow crumpled to its knees, sighed gustily and died.

Trembling with rage, the miller waited until the footsteps of Ogre faded away. Then he stood up, brushing seeds and straw from his hair. His wife sobbed beside him, for a cow was worth an inheritance to such people. But the miller, a practical man, simply got his knives and set about the business of skinning and dressing the animal. They could eat some of the meat and salt some of it; they would not starve. And they would certainly find a way to repay Ogre.

The next time the giant appeared in his yard, the miller was waiting. In lieu of grain or flour, he gave Ogre gold coins taken from a meager hoard concealed under the floor of the mill. Then he thanked his enemy for killing the cow. The hide, he said, had brought him several sacks of gold when he sold it.

Swinging his massive head slowly from side to side and rubbing his filthy hands along his tunic, Ogre considered the matter. He was unused to the idea of selling, but he came of a race that once had guarded treasure, and he well understood the glint of gold.

"The hide," said the miller slowly and distinctly. "When the cow was dead, I skinned it and sold the hide for gold."

Ogre nodded, then, and lumbered off. That night, the miller and his wife stood

A cruel churchman

The time came at last when giants and giant trolls were mastered not by human strength but by human trickery. Such was the case in Norway, where it was said that a cleric persuaded a mountain-dwelling troll to do the work of building a church. The price the priest offered was the sun, and the troll believed him.

The priest, of course, could not possibly have paid such a price and, indeed, never meant to. While the giant creature worked on the church, his employer wandered the mountains, searching for the troll's lair. He found it, and from within he heard the troll's female singing her companion's name. This was the weapon the priest needed: Trolls were an ancient race; their names were full of magic and not to be given into human keeping, for a mortal who knew a troll's name gained power over the old one.

The priest waited until the troll had put the finishing touches on the tower of the church. Then, standing below the structure while the creature balanced on the roof beam, he presented his treacherous payment. "Tvester," called the priest, shouting the secret name to the winds. The troll gave a horrible cry and fell to the ground, dying before he struck it.

With the howl of a mourning animal, one of the last giants of
France embraced the body of his life's companion. Tricked by an
unscrupulous human, the giant had murdered her.

outside the door of their cottage, shaking with laughter as the high-pitched bellowing of cattle echoed down from the hills: Ogre was slaughtering his herd.

Some weeks passed before Ogre returned to them, but when he did, the miller was waiting with a new trick, again involving parts of his cherished cow. The old one came down his mountain and pushed into the little cottage, a half-cured hide dangling from his hand. He waved the stinking thing in the miller's face and stammered, "No one would buy."

Without hesitation, the miller turned on his wife, shouting, "This is your doing, woman." He stabbed her in the breast. Blood spurted over her – chicken blood that filled the cow's bladder hidden beneath her shawl – and she sank to the floor.

Dropping the hide, Ogre shuffled to the woman and bent over her. He stared, breathing noisily through his mouth, and after a while he pointed and said, "Dead."

"So she is," replied the miller.

"Human killer," said Ogre, and his voice trailed off in a high, animal whine.

"Nonsense," said the miller. "It often happens, and it is a good lesson. Now, look." He picked up the bellows from his hearth, thrust the tip into his wife's mouth and pumped. The woman's breast rose and fell in response. She opened her eyes. He withdrew the bellows, and she sat up and said, "Forgive me, husband."

"Useful with females," said the miller.

"Old magic," said Ogre. "Give it to me."

"No magic without gold. Give me the coins I paid you."

Without a word, Ogre stumbled out. Half an hour later, he returned and poured onto the miller's floor not only the miller's savings but a pile of other, older coins as well: Like many giants, Ogre was a hoarder, and he could not count. The miller's eyes brightened at the sight, but he made no comment. Nodding as if to indicate that the transaction was a fair one, he handed over the bellows.

After hiding the gold away, the miller and his wife followed Ogre up into the hills, unable to resist witnessing the events that they had set in motion. They peered into the entrance of Ogre's smoky lair. Close by the hearth fire, the giant was arguing with his female. Lurching back and forth so that their shadows wavered and towered on the walls, they snarled and snapped unintelligibly. Finally, Ogre gave a shout. He picked up a knife and slashed his female's throat. With no more than a guttural moan and a spurt of blood, she fell into the fire.

Ogre stooped over her and shoved her away from the flames. He padded around her body, giving a peculiar gargling noise that might have been a laugh. Then he picked up the bellows. At the door, the miller nudged his wife.

Ogre used the bellows as the miller had. Although the breast of his female rose and fell as he pumped, her eyes did not open, and she did not stir. He tried again, and still she made no move. He sat her up. Her head lolled crazily. Frantic now, he shook her, but no shaking could awaken her.

At last, Ogre sank to the stones of the floor, still clutching the useless bellows. He cradled the body of his companion, rocking it back and forth, and loosed a high and wavering howl. The sorrow of the ages, of eternal loss and loneliness, reverberated in that cry.

At the door, the miller's wife plucked nervously at her husband's sleeve. Her eyes filled with tears, but the miller only shrugged. Then he led her home.

After that day, Ogre, now companionless, took to loitering around the mill, apparently unaware or uncaring that the miller was the author of his grief. From time to time, the miller amused himself by tricking the old creature, but he got little pleasure from it, and the sight of Ogre became an irritant. In the end, the miller lured the giant into the river by the mill, telling him that precious stones lay beneath the waters. There Ogre died, either because running water was often dangerous to beings of the old world or simply because he could not swim.

In this way—squalidly, victims of cruel jokes—the very last giants vanished from the earth. They who, at one time, had been masters of the deepest magic—illusionists and shape-shifters without equal—could now be fooled by a child's trick. No one mourned their passing.

Men and women told stories of giants, of course, and with a kind of patronizing nostalgia, they made images of them. Statues of Gogmagog—now split into two giants, Gog and Magog—long stood, as they still do, in the Guildhall of the London merchants, benignly overseeing the trade within. The citizens of Antwerp had a statue of Antigonus. Forty feet high, it was carved from wood and elaborately painted and gilded. The statue was hollow, and when it rode through the streets on a horse-drawn cart during municipal pageants and processions, a man stood inside, working the movable head so that the giant nodded back and forth.

Such figures, in fact, were common in Europe once. Merchants' and craftsmen's guilds of many cities—among them Brussels and Mons in Belgium and Douai in France—made models of giants to parade on public holidays such as religious feasts or royal processions. The Tailor's Company of Salisbury, in England, had a figure twelve feet high. It was made of laths and hoops, with a pasteboard head; it wore drapery of red and purple chintz and a gold-laced hat, and a pipe was stuck into its mouth.

Great trouble was taken to keep such pasteboard giants' decoration in repair, as the expense books of the Butchers' Guild of Chester show: There were entries indicating payment for cloth and buckram, for foil, for gold and silver leaf, for glue and paste. There also exists the following sad ledger item: "For arsenic to put into the paste to save the giants from being eaten by rats, one shilling and fourpence."

It was a pathetic ending for the mighty creatures, to be paraded as puppets before laughing humanity and guarded against the hunger of vermin. Yet there was another kind of souvenir of the days of the giants. Countryfolk knew it: They would point to certain hills, to riverbeds and gorges and say that these were the marks of the old ones, whose great hands had helped shape the earth.

Solitary hills rising from plains were suggestive of the work of giants. Legend held that one sad-eyed German giantess, hearing that mortals would destroy her race, raised a mountain on the flats of Brandenburg to block their

The Earth's Memory

Long after the last giants vanished from the earth, their imprints lingered on the landscape, souvenirs of an age of wonders. The trails where generations of giants trod were marked by mountain clefts and winding valleys. The footprints of giants formed lake beds, and massive boulders lay where giants had hurled them in sport or in anger. No doubt some of nature's own handiwork was mistakenly ascribed to giants, but many features of the planet seemed to lend themselves to no other explanation.

way. With no tools but her hands, she scooped and sculpted, and then she spiked the earthen barrier with trees and stones. It was a pitiable effort, in truth — and the mountain was more an object of amazement than an impediment

At the land's ending in the north of Ireland, the folk of Ulster say, a giant once stared out to sea for days at a time, pining for a woman of the isle of Staffa in the distant Hebrides. Finally he set to work, placing thick stone columns

side by side to build a road across the water so that he might reach his love. Whether the giant achieved his goal is
not known, but a fragment of that causeway stands there still, yearning out toward Staffa, a hundred miles away.

A deep canyon slashing a mountainside in the central highlands of Norway was said to have been made by a giant troll who schemed to divert the waters of the River Glomma down to Rendalen, his native valley far below.

The troll, however, had a jealous neighbor, a behemoth who watched over the river, and this creature slew the would-be thief of the waters. So the troll canyon was unfinished and the river continued to flow in its rightful bed.

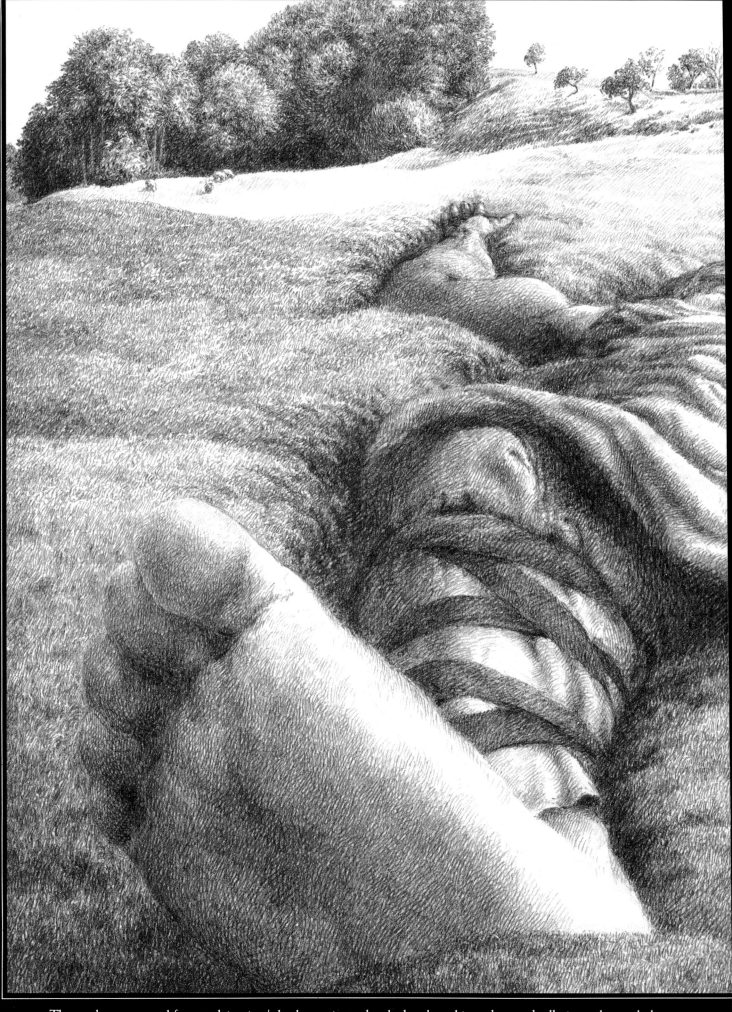

The earth was created from a slain giant's body, ancient tales declared, and into that earth all giants descended when their day was done. One British giant – measuring 240 feet from crown to toe – left his form on the Sussex hill

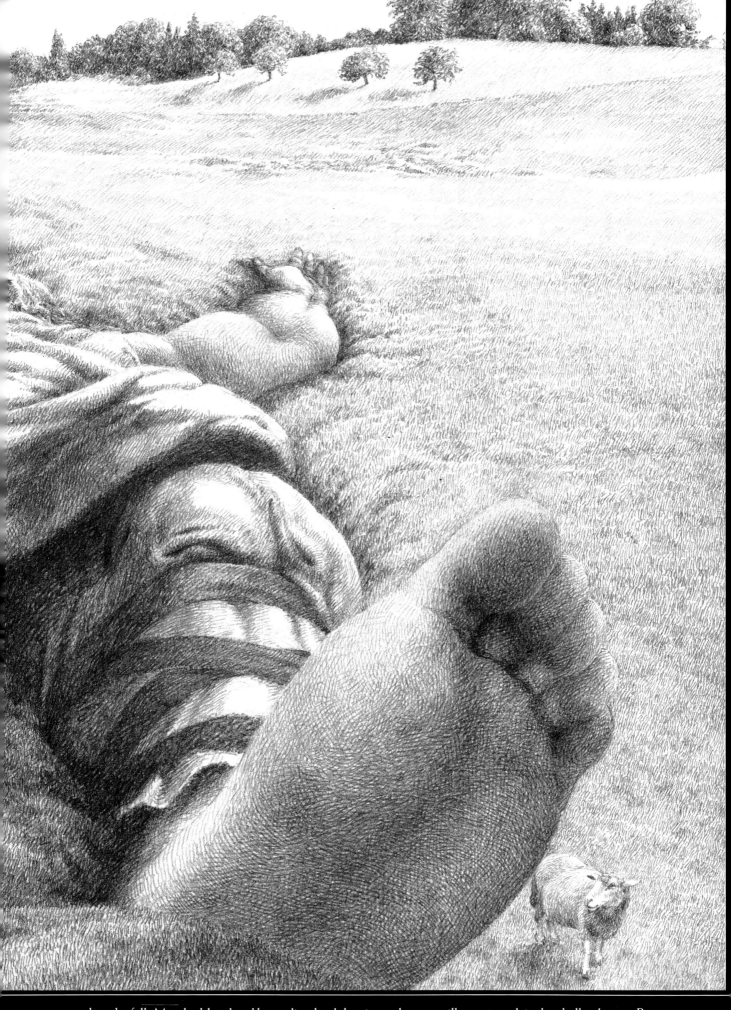

where he fell. Muscle, blood and bone dissolved, leaving only a vast silhouette sunk in the chalky downs. Peasants
called him the Long Man of Wilmington, and grazed their sheep about the massive legs and wide-flung arms.

The hilly coast of the Baltic island of Rügen had its origin in a giant's misfortune. In order that he might cross dry-
shod from his island to the shore of Pomerania, the fellow thought to fill the sea in between. But the bulging sack in

which he hauled the stones he had collected for the task was ripped open by the steeple of a church; the great
stones fell out, to be wasted as a line of useless hills. At that, the giant quit in vexation and left the area for good.

Picture Credits

The sources for the illustrations in this book are shown below. When known, the name of the artist precedes the picture source.

Cover: Artwork by Roberto Innocenti. 1-5: Artwork by Alicia Austin. 6, 7: Artwork by Donna Neary. 10, 11: Hermann Knopf, courtesy Westfälisches Landesmuseum für Kunst und Kulturgeschichte, photo Atelier Wiegel-Bracht, Münster. 13: Francisco Goya, courtesy Museo del Prado, Madrid, photographed by Scala, Florence. 14, 15: Nicolas Poussin, courtesy the Metropolitan Museum of Art, Fletcher Fund, 1924. 16-23: Artwork by John Howe. 24-27: Artwork by Donna Neary. 30-41: Artwork by Matt Mahurin. 42, 43: Artwork by Roberto Innocenti. 47: Russian Museum, Leningrad, photographed by VAAP, Moscow. 50, 51: Artwork by Julek Heller. 54, 55: Artwork by John Howe. 56-59: Artwork by Julek Heller. 60, 61: Artwork by John Howe. 62: Artwork by Julek Heller. 64, 65: Artwork by John Howe. 66, 67: Artwork by Julek Heller. 68-77: Artwork by Alicia Austin. 78-83: Artwork by Matt Mahurin. 85: Edmund Dulac, copyright Geraldine M. Anderson, from *Sinbad the Sailor and Other Stories from the Arabian Nights*, Hodder and Stoughton, 1914, courtesy the British Museum and the Bridgeman Art Library, London. 89: Artwork by Yvonne Gilbert. 90, 91: Artwork by James C. Christensen. 93-95: Artwork by John Jude Palencar. 96-101: Artwork by Barry Moser. 102-109: Artwork by Matt Mahurin. 110, 111: Artwork by Donna Neary. 114: Alessandro Allori, courtesy Banca Toscana Palace, Florence, photographed by Erich Lessing from Magnum, Paris. 116, 117: Foto Catalogue Arnold Böcklin, courtesy Mathildenhöhe, Darmstadt, 1977. 120: N. C. Wyeth, from *The Legends of Charlemagne* by Thomas Bulfinch, Cosmopolitan Book Corporation, New York, 1924. 122, 123: Artwork by John Howe. 125: Artwork by Roberto Innocenti. 126, 127: Artwork by Matt Mahurin. 130-139: Artwork by Willi Glasauer. 144: Artwork by Alicia Austin.

Bibliography

Afanas'ev, Aleksandr, *Russian Fairy Tales*. Transl. by Norbert Guterman. New York: Pantheon Books, 1975.

Baly, Denis, *The Geography of the Bible: A Study in Historical Geography*. New York: Harper & Row, 1957.

Bauer, John, *Great Swedish Fairy Tales*. New York: Delacorte Press/Seymour Lawrence, 1978 (reprint of 1973 edition).

Beach, Milo Cleveland, *The Adventures of Rama*. Washington, D.C.: Freer Gallery of Art, Smithsonian Institution, 1983.

Bett, Henry, *Nursery Rhymes and Tales: Their Origin and History*. London: Norwood Editions, 1978 (reprint of 1924 edition).

Bologna, Gianfranco, *Simon and Schuster's Guide to Birds of the World*. Ed. by John Bull, transl. by Arnoldo Mondadori. New York: Simon and Schuster, 1981.

Brewer's Dictionary of Phrase and Fable. Revised by Ivor H. Evans. New York: Harper & Row, 1970.

Briggs, Katharine M., *A Dictionary of British Folk-Tales in the English Language*. Vol. 1, *Folk Legends*. London: Routledge & Kegan Paul, 1971.

Briggs, Katharine M., and Ruth L. Tongue, eds., *Folktales of England*. Chicago: The University of Chicago Press, 1965.

Bringsværd, Tor Age, *Phantoms and Fairies from Norwegian Folklore*. Transl. by Pat Shaw Iversen. Oslo: Johan Grundt Tanum Forlag, no date.*

Broderius, John R., "The Giant in Germanic Tradition." Dissertation. Chicago: The University of Chicago Libraries, 1932.*

Bromwich, Rachel, ed. and transl., *Trioedd Ynys Prydein (The Welsh Triads)*. Cardiff: University of Wales Press, 1961.

Bruce, James Douglas, *The Evolution of Arthurian Romance: From the Beginnings Down to the Year 1300*. Vols. 1 and 2. Gloucester, Massachusetts: Peter Smith, 1958 (reprint of 1928 edition).

Bulfinch, Thomas:
Bulfinch's Mythology. New York: The Modern Library, no date.*
Legends of Charlemagne. New York: Cosmopolitan Book Corporation, 1924.
Myths of Greece and Rome. Comp. by Bryan Holme. New York: Penguin Books, 1981.

Cavendish, Richard, ed., *Man, Myth & Magic*. 11 vols. New York: Marshall Cavendish, 1983.

Chrétien de Troyes, *Arthurian Romances*. Transl. by W. Wistar Comfort. London: J. M. Dent & Sons, 1913.*

Craigie, William Alexander, ed. and transl., *Scandinavian Folk-Lore*. Detroit: Singing Tree Press, 1970 (reprint of 1896 edition).

Crossley-Holland, Kevin, *The Norse Myths*. New York: Pantheon Books, 1980.*

The Cruikshank Fairy-Book. New York: G. P. Putnam's Sons, 1969.

Cunliffe, Barry, *The Celtic World.* New York: McGraw-Hill, 1979.

D'Aulaire, Ingri, and Edgar Parin d'Aulaire, *Norse Gods and Giants.* Garden City, New York: Doubleday, 1967.

Davidson, Hilda R. Ellis, *Gods and Myths of Northern Europe.* New York: Penguin Books, 1982.

Downing, Charles, *Russian Tales and Legends.* Oxford, England: Oxford University Press, 1978.

Fairholt, F. W., *Gog and Magog: The Giants in Guildhall.* London: John Camden Hotten, 1859.*

Ford, Patrick K., transl., *The Mabinogi and Other Medieval Welsh Tales.* Berkeley: University of California Press, 1977.

Frazer, Sir James George, *The New Golden Bough.* Ed. by Theodor H. Gaster. New York: New American Library, Mentor, 1964.

Gallant, Roy A., *The Constellations: How They Came to Be.* New York: Four Winds Press, 1979.

Gantz, Jeffrey, transl., *The Mabinogion.* New York: Penguin Books, 1981.*

Graham, Winston, *Poldark's Cornwall.* London and Exeter: The Bodley Head and Webb & Bower, 1983.

Graves, Robert, *The Greek Myths.* Vols. 1 and 2. New York: Penguin Books, 1983.

Hammond, N.G.L., and H. H. Scullard, *The Oxford Classical Dictionary.* Oxford, England: Oxford University Press, 1978.

Homer, *The Odyssey of Homer.* Transl. by Ennis Rees. New York: The Modern Library, 1960.*

Jacobs, Joseph, comp., *English Fairy Tales.* New York: Dover Publications, 1967.

Johnson, Hugh, *The International Book of Trees.* London: Mitchell Beazley Publishers, 1980.

Jones, Gwyn, and Thomas Jones, transls., *The Mabinogion.* Hendrik-Ido-Ambacht, The Netherlands: Dragon's Dream B. V., 1982.*

Kightly, Charles, *Folk Heroes of Britain.* New York: Thames and Hudson, 1982.

Lanier, Henry Wysham, *A Book of Giants: Tales of Very Tall Men of Myth, Legend, History, and Science* (The Library of Romance series). New York: E. P. Dutton, 1922.

Leach, Maria, ed., *Funk & Wagnalls Standard Dictionary of Folklore, Mythology and Legend.* 2 vols. San Francisco: Harper & Row, 1949.

Lindow, John, *Swedish Legends and Folktales.* Berkeley: University of California Press, 1978.

Loomis, Roger Sherman, ed., *Arthurian Literature in the Middle Ages.* London: Oxford University Press, 1961.

MacCulloch, John Arnott, *The Mythology of All Races: Eddic.* Vol. 2. New York: Cooper Square, 1964.

Marden, Luis, "Sicily the Three-Cornered." *The National Geographic Magazine,* January 1955.

Marsden, Walter, *Lapland* (The World's Wild Places series). Amsterdam: Time-Life Books, 1976.

Mayne, William, ed., *The Hamish Hamilton Book of Giants.* London: Hamish Hamilton, 1968.

Moorman, Charles, and Ruth Moorman, *An Arthurian Dictionary.* Jackson, Mississippi: University Press of Mississippi, 1978.

National Geographic Atlas of the World. Washington, D.C.: National Geographic Society, 1970.

The New Illustrated Columbia Encyclopedia. Garden City, New York: Rockville House, 1979.

Nicolson, Adam, *The National Trust Book of Long Walks in England, Scotland and Wales.* New York: Harmony Books, 1981.

Opie, Iona, and Peter Opie, *The Classic Fairy Tales.* New York: Oxford University Press, 1974.

Picard, Barbara Leonie, *French Legends, Tales and Fairy Stories.* London: Oxford University Press, 1975.

Polunin, Oleg, *Flowers of Europe: A Field Guide.* London: Oxford University Press, 1969.

Reader's Digest Association, *Discovering Britain.* London: Drive Publications, 1982.

Ross, Anne, *Pagan Celtic Britain: Studies in Iconography and Tradition.* London: Routledge and Kegan Paul, 1967.

Shor, Jean, and Franc Shor, "North with Finland's Lapps." *The National Geographic Magazine,* August 1954.

Spicer, Dorothy Gladys, *13 Giants.* New York: Coward-McCann, 1966.

Stone, Brian, transl., *Sir Gawain and the Green Knight.* New York: Penguin Books, 1974.*

Surmelian, Leon, *Daredevils of Sassoun: The Armenian National Epic.* Denver: Alan Swallow, 1964.*

Teale, Sarah, *Giants.* New York: Harry N. Abrams, 1979.

Thompson, Stith, ed., *One Hundred Favorite Folktales.* Bloomington, Indiana: Indiana University Press, 1968.

Tolegian, Aram, transl., *David of Sassoun: Armenian Folk Epic.* New York: Bookman Associates, 1961.

Tongue, Ruth L., comp., *Forgotten Folk-tales of the English Counties.* London: Routledge & Kegan Paul, 1970.

Vaughan-Thomas, Wynford, *Wales.* London: Michael Joseph, 1983.

Wheeler, Alwyne, *The Fishes of the British Isles and North-West Europe.* London: Macmillan, 1969.

Wood, Edward J., *Giants and Dwarfs.* Darby, Pennsylvania: Folcroft Library Editions, 1974.

Titles marked with an asterisk were especially helpful in the preparation of this volume.

Acknowledgments

The editors wish to thank the following persons and institutions for their help in the preparation of this volume: Ancilla Antonini, Scala, Florence; François Avril, Curator, Département des Manuscrits, Bibliothèque Nationale, Paris; Countess Maria Fede Caproni, Rome; Moussia Devambez, Paris; Manfred Eger, Richard-Wagner-Museum, Bayreuth; Claude Gaignebet, Paris; Marielise Göpel, Archiv für Kunst und Geschichte, West Berlin; Kenichiro Hashimoto, Kanagawa Prefectural Museum, Yokohama; Dieter Hennig, Director, Brüder Grimm-Museum, Kassel; Gustav Henningsen, Research Director, Danish Folklore Archives, Copenhagen; Michael Heseltine, Sotheby's, London; Christine Hofmann, Bayerische Staatsgemäldesammlungen, Munich; Keio Gijuku Toshokan, Tokyo; Seigfried Kessemeier, Westfälisches Landesmuseum für Kunst und Kulturgeschichte, Münster; Heidi Klein, Bildarchiv Preussischer Kulturbesitz, West Berlin; Waltraud von Kries, Westfälisches Landesmuseum für Kunst und Kulturgeschichte, Münster; Bernd Krimmel, Director, Mathildenhöhe, Darmstadt; J. P. Losty, Assistant Keeper, Department of Oriental Manuscripts and Printed Books, British Library, London; Bernd Meier, Kunstbibliothek, West Berlin, Agnès Nercessian, C. N. R. S. - L. I. M. C., Paris; Christine Poulson, London; B. W. Robinson, London; M. Rogers, Deputy Keeper, Department of Oriental Antiquities, British Museum, London; Véronique Schiltz, Paris; Seikado Bunko, Tokyo; Mitsuhiko Shibata, Atomi University, Tokyo; R. W. Skelton, Keeper, Indian Section, Victoria and Albert Museum, London; Soviet Copyright Agency, Moscow; Jinichi Suzuki, Tokyo.

TIME-LIFE BOOKS

EUROPEAN EDITOR: Kit van Tulleken
Assistant European Editor: Gillian Moore
Design Director: Ed Skyner
Photography Director: Pamela Marke
Chief of Research: Vanessa Kramer
Chief Sub-Editor: Ilse Gray

THE ENCHANTED WORLD

SERIES DIRECTOR: Ellen Phillips
Deputy Editor: Robin Richman
Designer: Dale Pollekoff
Chief Researcher: Jane Edwin

Editorial Staff for *Giants and Ogres*
Staff Writers: Daniel Stashower, Donia Ann Steele
Researcher: Trudy Pearson
Assistant Designer: Lorraine D. Rivard
Copy Coordinators: Barbara Fairchild Quarmby, Robert Somerville
Picture Coordinator: Nancy C. Scott
Editorial Assistant: Constance B. Strawbridge

Correspondents: Elisabeth Kraemer-Singh (Bonn); Margot Hapgood, Dorothy Bacon (London); Miriam Hsia (New York); Maria Vincenza Aloisi, Josephine du Brusle (Paris); Ann Natanson (Rome). Valuable assistance was also provided by: Brigid Grauman (Brussels); Ardis Grosjean (Copenhagen); Judy Aspinall (London); Trini Bandrés (Madrid); Felix Rosenthal (Moscow); Carolyn Chubet (New York); Dag Christensen (Oslo); Mary Johnson (Stockholm); Traudl Lessing (Vienna).

Editorial Production
Production Assistants: Nikki Allen, Alan Godwin, Maureen Kelly
Editorial Department: Theresa John, Debra Lelliott

Chief Series Consultant

Tristram Potter Coffin, Professor of English at the University of Pennsylvania, is a leading authority on folklore. He is the author or editor of numerous books and more than 100 articles. His best-known works are *The British Traditional Ballad in North America*, *The Old Ball Game*, *The Book of Christmas Folklore* and *The Female Hero*.

This volume is one of a series that is based on myths, legends and folk tales.

TIME
LIFE
BOOKS

THE ENCHANTED WORLD
LIBRARY OF NATIONS
HOME REPAIR AND IMPROVEMENT
CLASSICS OF EXPLORATION
PLANET EARTH
PEOPLES OF THE WILD
THE EPIC OF FLIGHT
THE SEAFARERS
WORLD WAR II
THE GOOD COOK
THE TIME-LIFE ENCYCLOPAEDIA OF GARDENING
THE GREAT CITIES
THE OLD WEST
THE WORLD'S WILD PLACES
THE EMERGENCE OF MAN
LIFE LIBRARY OF PHOTOGRAPHY
TIME-LIFE LIBRARY OF ART
GREAT AGES OF MAN
LIFE SCIENCE LIBRARY
LIFE NATURE LIBRARY
THE TIME-LIFE BOOK OF BOATING
TECHNIQUES OF PHOTOGRAPHY
LIFE AT WAR
LIFE GOES TO THE MOVIES
BEST OF LIFE
LIFE IN SPACE

PRINTED AND BOUND BY BREPOLS S.A.-TURNHOUT, BELGIUM

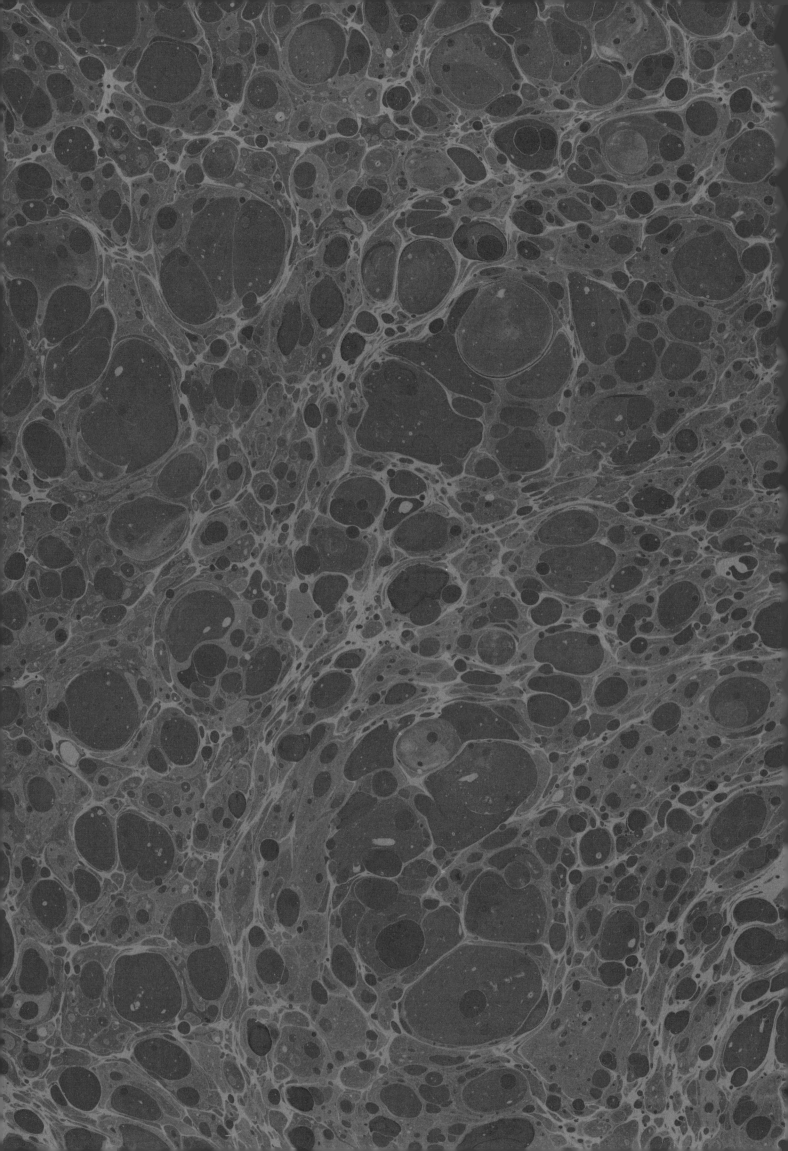